50

Popular
Research Narratives

*Fifty five-minute stories of research,
invention, or discovery, directly
from the "men who did it,"
pithily told in language
for laymen, young
and old*

By

Slosson, Edwin E. and others.

COLLECTED BY THE
ENGINEERING FOUNDATION
29 West 39th Street, New York
and for it done into a book

by

WILLIAMS & WILKINS COMPANY
BALTIMORE, MARYLAND
1924

TABLE OF NARRATIVES

HOW SCIENCE GROWS

By Edwin E. Slosson

Director of Science Service, Washington

Botany took a boom in this country in 1858 when Asa Gray published a little book called "How Plants Grow." It was an epoch-making work for previous text-books had dealt most with description of the dried specimens in the herbarium or at any rate with the fully formed flower. You could hardly tell a book on botany from a book on mineralogy except by the title on the back.

But when the people caught the idea that the plant was a growing thing, somewhat similar to themselves, they waked up to the fact that plants were interesting to watch. The wide-awake realtor knows this trait of human nature and he sets up a sign by the railroad station reading "Watch Boomville Grow!"

Director Flinn of Engineering Foundation knows human nature too and so he has got out these "Research Narratives" which present science as a growing vital thing, not as a cut and dried set of algebraic formulas. He has put personality into these sketches. One of the reasons why science is caviar to the general public, is that it has been so conscientiously depersonalized. The effort is constantly made to reduce science to a set of mathematic formulas, free from all taint of time, place, and personality, bearing no trace of its erratic history and early gropings in the dark.

This is quite a proper procedure for the development of a science, no doubt, but it has an unfortunate effect that in eliminating the human element we have eliminated the human interest. Chemically pure sucrose is a beautiful product, a triumph of technology in which the chemist may well take pride, but it is not so tasty as maple sap or cane juice. It has lost its vitamins. To put a modern high-grade textbook in the hands of the ordinary reader is like feeding decorticated rice to a soldier. It gives him mental beriberi. I hope I shall not be misunderstood as saying anything against the chemist's constant efforts to achieve a higher degree of purification. Perfect purity is a noble aim even though it be asymptotically unattainable to human beings. There was once a little girl who prayed "O God, make me pure; make me absolutely pure like Royal Baking Powder!" Now it does not do any harm for baking powder to be pure because it gets mixed with so many other things, but if the flour is absolutely pure, and the fat and the salt and the water, well, somehow the bread is not so nutritious as it might be.

I am not sure that even in a textbook a bit of history or a few personalities would be out of place, though they might give the student the idea that the principles of the science have been worked out by slow degrees and much blundering by fallible human beings instead of being handed down in perfect form on tables of stone like the Ten Commandments. But anyhow, I am sure that for the general reader it is best not to refine too highly but to leave in a little of the human alloy.

These little "Research Narratives" in their original leaflet form were convenient to stuff into one's pocket and to stow into one's head. But because they were so handy to carry about and to give away, I have never been able to keep a complete file of them. So I am glad to see them in a more permanent but no less portable form. I have stolen more ideas from them than I have publicly acknowledged for they often contain technical and personal information hard to find elsewhere. Textbooks, monographs and encyclopedias contain the past and public data of science but these "Research Narratives" bring news from the terminal tip of its fast-growing shoots.

ENGINEERING FOUNDATION

In 1914, Ambrose Swasey, of Cleveland, Ohio, offered the four American societies of Civil, Mining and Metallurgical, Mechanical, and Electrical Engineers the nucleus of an endowment for a joint research organization. This was the beginning of Engineering Foundation. It was created "for the furtherance of research in science and in engineering, or for the advancement in any other manner of the profession of engineering and the good of mankind."

Many years ago, Mr. Swasey and his friend, Worcester R. Warner, established the Warner and Swasey Company, which has built fine machine tools, great telescopes and precision instruments. He was one of the organizers of the American Society of Mechanical Engineers, later its president, and is now an honorary member of that society, of the American Society of Civil Engineers and of other important bodies in the United States and abroad. Recently he was awarded the John Fritz Gold Medal, the highest honor bestowed by the engineering profession in America. Ambrose Swasey was born on a farm in New Hampshire in 1846 and is still a leader in good works. To him these Narratives are dedicated.

Research, invention and discovery are vital to the progress of modern peoples. Scientists and engineers, however, habitually write in language which conceals fascinating achievements from the uninitiated. That a nation may advance, its intelligent citizens at least must have an appreciation of the gains made by science and a realization of the need for more knowledge of nature—for research. To promote interest in these subjects Engineering Foundation began in 1921 the semi-monthly printing of very short stories in lay language from original sources. Here are the first fifty. When there are fifty more—a year hence—there may be another book.

AMBROSE SWASEY
Founder of Engineering Foundation

ISOLATED RESEARCH: ITS HANDICAPS

The Story of Mendelism

Gregor Mendel was an Austrian monk who became interested in botanical research. About the year 1860, he studied in the gardens of the monastery at Brünn the laws of heredity as displayed in the common vegetable pea plants. This study led him to the discovery of the wonderful doctrine of the inheritance of unit characters among plants and animals, which doctrine has since become famous as the Mendelian theory, or Mendelism. Yet, owing to an unhappy mischance in the course of his researches, he lost confidence in his results and almost failed to transmit their message to the world.

Mendel hit upon a sound method of attacking the problem of plant inheritance, by selecting a single, but easily recognized, quality for his investigation; namely, plant stature. He crossed tall peas with dwarf peas, and watched the hybrid offspring in its subsequent generations of normal propagation. The hybrids were all tall in the first generation. But in subsequent generations, one-quarter of the plants bred true as tall peas, one-quarter bred true as dwarf peas, and half developed variations, or were uncertain. To account for this remarkable tall behavior of the first generation, he invented the notion that a quality like tallness may be "dominant" and shortness "recessive" thereto; while the germ cells, or "gametes," are nevertheless transmitted faithfully by each member of the race. A large literature and

1

field of research has been developed along these lines, since Mendel's time, both in plants and in animals.

Mendel having satisfied himself as to the behavior of peas in the matter of tall and short inheritance, after many generations of peas in his monastery garden, aspired to repeat his results and check his deductions among other plants from the outside world. There were, doubtless, hundreds of different plants available. He happened to choose the hawkweed, a common plant of the dandelion family. Why he selected this particular plant is not known. Unfortunately, however, this plant is one of the very few that obey in reproduction a very special law, in that they are self-fertilizing, or subject to "parthenogenesis." In all probability, Mendel did not know of this condition; but it was sufficient to make a failure of his attempt at crossing two varieties. Apparently his theory was refuted by these rebellious flowers.

It was only a chance of perhaps one in a thousand that Mendel selected for his control experiment a parthenogetic flower, on which his efforts would necessarily be futile. On almost any other flower but this, he would probably have succeeded. His failure so discouraged him that instead of announcing his results to the principal botanical and biological societies, he communicated only a modest paper on his garden-pea researches to a small local society in 1865; so that it was not until about 1900, or more than a generation later, that the Mendelian doctrine became known to the scientific world.

One moral to this story is that there is certainly an element of luck in the affairs of men, and that Mendel certainly had bad luck in his choice of a control experiment for checking scientific results.

Another moral is that researches may be in many cases, but not all, with advantage, conducted associatively, as distinguished from individually. If any scientific research council could have been apprized of Mendel's garden-pea results, the prosecution of further investigations would have been dealt with by group methods, and no single mischance of the hawkweed type would have stolen away their confidence. The world would then have known of this principle thirty years sooner. It is in research, as it is in other things of line: *L'union fait la force.*

This narrative was contributed by Arthur E. Kennelly, A.M., D.Sc., Professor of Electrical Engineering, Harvard University and Massachusetts Institute of Technology.

FATIGUE OF METALS

A Story of Coöperation

Do the metals get tired? In school-days we "orated" about tireless "steel-sinewed" athletes. Now, forsooth, the word "fatigue" is being used by men of science as the most suggestive name for certain kinds of failures of steel and other metals. Metal of apparently excellent quality breaks without warning in crank-shafts of airplanes, in parts of steam turbines, in other rapidly moving machines, in members of bridges subjected to vibration and frequent changes of stress. What are the causes? How can such failures be avoided? What are the limits of endurance of various metals under many repetitions of stress?

Answers to these questions became especially important during the war, and particularly in connection with military aviation. A committee of engineers and scientists organized by National Research Council and Engineering Foundation undertook a study. The problem proved complex and its study costly. But lives and property are in jeopardy through lack of knowledge. Therefore, the study has been continued. After the armistice, the Division of Engineering of National Research Council turned to Engineering Foundation for financial assistance. The Engineering Experiment Station of the University of Illinois had been connected with the early study and had the men and some of the facilities needed for further research.

In October, 1919, the three organizations mentioned entered into an agreement for two years, Engineering Founda-

4

tion undertaking to provide $30,000 in installments as needed. A limited line of experiments was inaugurated. Certain manufacturers contributed test specimens of steel. Special machines were constructed and methods devised. Under known conditions many specimens are being subjected to millions of repetitions or changes of stress. Information of practical importance is emerging from the accumulating records of hundreds of observations.

In the fall of 1920, the General Electric Company requested an extension of the program of tests to cover certain nickel steels in which it is interested as a builder of steam turbines. To meet the expense, the Company offered $30,000. A supplementary agreement was undertaken and the new work has been started. The company gets, incidentally, the benefits of the experience already gained, the special facilities developed, and the general supervision of the committee of expert metallurgists and testing engineers, organized for this research by National Research Council and Engineering Foundation.

Other users and producers of wrought or cast metals can secure valuable information at relatively small cost, by taking advantage of the existing staff and facilities for expanding this research in fields of peculiar interest to them. Each group of special tests helps in the understanding of the general problem.

This coöperative research is an example of one of the most effective uses for the funds of Engineering Foundation. By a relatively modest expenditure, the Foundation initiated the tests and carried them far enough to demonstrate their usefulness to the industries concerned; through the affiliation between the Foundation and the Research Council, the advice of the leading men of science in this field is contributed for the determination of methods and the interpretation of results. Similar procedure can be applied to other kinds of researches.

Engineering Foundation is willing to function in this manner to the extent that the resources put at its disposal will permit. It could use larger funds than it now has.

Based upon information from Prof. H. F. Moore, Engineering Experiment Station, University of Illinois, Urbania, Ill., in charge of the research on Fatigue Phenomena of Metals.

In 1924, this research is being continued. The number of coöperating companies has increased. Valuable results have been gotten. Three interesting technical reports have been published. Other laboratories, also, are investigating this important subject.

UTILIZING LOW-GRADE ORES

An Iron Story

This is the Iron Age. An Aluminum Age may follow; but its sun is far below the eastern horizon.

Iron is essential to the present high degree of usefulness and independence which the United States enjoys among the nations of the world. Necessary production and improvement of iron and steel depend upon research by metallurgists, chemists, physicists, engineers and geologists.

Each year there are consumed in the United States about 75,000,000 tons of iron ore. Methods of smelting now in vogue demand ore containing 50 per cent or more of iron. Known deposits meeting this requirement are being rapidly depleted. To be sure, they will last many years. But what next? One answer is: New deposits of rich ore may be found in our country; but the search has already been diligent. If found, rich ore bodies may not be advantageously situated in respect to transportation, blast furnaces or steel mills. A second reply is: Import; there are rich ore deposits in other countries, some of which are already controlled by Americans. Some objections are obvious, especially in times of national defense, when iron is most needed.

A third solution of this problem has long been sought by scientists and inventors. Large sums of money have been devoted to experiments. Success at length seems assured. What is it? The economic utilization of low-grade ores. There are vast deposits of such iron ores conveniently situated as to transportation and existing iron and steel industries.

Mr. D. C. Jackling and associated engineers, members of the American Institute of Mining and Metallurgical Engineers, after exhaustive research, followed by experiments on a semi-commercial scale, have developed a practical process. Five years of hard work were necessary, in which all previous knowledge was utilized, and hundreds of thousands of dollars were spent.

Large quantities of low-grade ores are of the magnetic variety. It is to such ores that the new process applies. There are estimated to be many billions of tons. These ores are to be quarried in huge quantities, crushed and ground, and then the iron-bearing particles separated from the remainder by electro-magnetic methods. This selected portion is sintered (partially fused so as to form masses) and crushed to convenient size. A rich concentrate results, in acceptable condition for the blast furnace.

Extended experience in mining and working these lean ores will, doubtless, bring improvements, and, with continued research, great economies may be effected. This beneficiating of low-grade iron ores, so as to make them usable, must be accomplished if the United States is to continue to hold its position as a steel producer on the present scale. The studies have not been confined to any single ore deposit. Ores from many localities have been put through the tests. Machinery and methods of great value to the iron and steel industry, as a whole, have been developed. The first unit (costing $4,000,000) of a large plant for the concentration of these low-grade ores is under construction in Minnesota. The cost of the complete plant has been put at $60,000,000; its capacity would be 100,000 tons of rock daily, yielding 40,000 tons of concentrates.

Research is sometimes costly; but wisely directed, it pays. The whole world is benefited.

For the information in this Narrative Engineering Foundation is indebted to Mr. W. G. Swart, Mining and Metallurgical Engineer, Duluth, Minnesota.

ELECTRIC WELDING

FROM LECTURE ROOM TO INDUSTRY

In 1877, Professor Thomson delivered at the Franklin Institute, Philadelphia, five lectures on electricity. The object of the lectures and the demonstrations, which latter were numerous and many of them original even to the employment of special apparatus constructed by the lecturer, was to show clearly that electricity, of whatever name, was the same, differing only in tension (as it was termed) and in the current flowing, or quantity (the old term), in steadiness or in wave-like character. In those days, the text-books divided the subject into statical and dynamic electricity, with sub-divisions such as frictional electricity, voltaic electricity, magneto electricity, electromagnetism, thermo electricity, and animal electricity. The well-known Ruhmkorff coil, or spark coil as it is now called (as when used for the ignition of automobiles), was employed to step up a battery current to a high-tension discharge which would charge condensers, such as Leyden jars.

Having made such demonstrations, the lecturer conceived the idea of reversing the process, charging some large Leyden jars by a power-driven static machine, and then arranging to pass the discharge of this large Leyden jar condenser through the fine wire, or secondary winding, of the ignition coil. The primary of such coil (which was, of course, of heavy wire) had its terminals disengaged and put lightly into contact. It was found on the discharge of the condenser through the fine wire that these heavy primary wires stuck together permanently. They had been welded by the passage of a practically instantaneous discharge of a very heavy current. In modern language it may be said that the condenser current, which was one of extremely high voltage and small flow (perhaps only a fraction of an ampere), had been transformed down, producing in the primary a current of only a few volts, but of great strength in amperes, so that the instantaneous local heating of the ends of the primary coil, which were in contact, brought them to the point of fusion, and union took place.

Such an observation made by one who was paying little attention to possibilities might have escaped notice. Not so with the lecturer. He at once saw the possibilities of transforming a high-voltage current down to reduced voltage, and causing thereby the union of metals. He had, in fact, the conception, in a crude way it is true, of what finally became his process of electric welding. Prevented by many demands on time from carrying this simple suggestion further, he constantly bore it in mind, and on the inception of the business which afterwards became the large Thomson-Houston enterprise, he discussed the possibility of proceeding with electric welding.

In 1885, the opportunity came to complete the conception of the earlier days. An alternating-current generator being at disposition, it was only necessary to construct an induction coil, or transformer, in which the primary was of many turns adapted to the output of the generator, while the secondary had only very few turns, but the section of which was so large that a great flow of current was possible. Connected to the heavy secondary terminals was a set of clamps for holding pieces of metal to be welded. The projecting portions of these metal bars were brought together with some pressure and the current turned on by closing the switch in the primary, there being arrangements for regulating the amount of primary current flowing. The very heavy, low-voltage current in the secondary immediately heated the metal pieces at their junction, so that they softened and united. Thus were the first electric welds made, and thus also the original suggestion during the scientific demonstrations at the Franklin Institute bore fruit, finally becoming the basis of the enormous extension in welding now existing. The modest apparatus was soon followed by welding transformers for large work; those were the first transformers in which the secondary constituted only a single turn, a characteristic of most of the welding transformers of today.

In the early days of the American Electric Company, in New Britain (afterwards the Thomson-Houston Company, with works in Lynn, Massachusetts), it was found impossible to get any considerable lengths of insulated copper wire for the winding of field magnets of the dynamos being constructed, without having to suffer the risk and inconvenience of numerous brazed joints irregular in outline and liable to cause puncture or leakage between layers, and breakdown. Professor Thomson, remonstrating with the wire manufacturers, was told that it was a necessary consequence of the production of copper wire, which was made from rolled sheets by shearing them into very narrow strips of almost square section and then drawing these through dies to make them round. One can well imagine that such wire would not be free from slivers sticking through the insulation, and this was often the case. But each strip, as explained by the manufacturer, could not exceed nine pounds; a coil of 200 pounds would have at least 22 joints. The ends of each nine-pound strip were tapered, or scarfed, while the wire was bare, and then hard-soldered with brass and the joints roughly filed (not drawn) subsequent to joining; then the whole was wrapped with cotton insulation, with the result that every joint was a lump of varied contour, which had to receive, in winding on a field magnet, reinforcements of insulation. Every sliver, too, had to be sought out and reinforced with insulation, or removed, but the chief objection was the numerous rough joints. Professor Thomson had enjoined the copper wire manufacturer to weld his joints and then draw the wire. The answer was, "Oh, copper cannot be welded,—that is impossible." The rejoinder was, "Oh yes, it can. I have a method which will do it." These words were made good later, when in the construction of large lengths of copper wire the electric welder was employed to unite copper to copper, the pieces so united being afterwards reduced in section by the drawing process. Of course, copper welding by the Thomson process is now, and has been for many years, a common operation.

This Narrative was contributed by Dr. Elihu Thomson, Consulting Engineer, General Electric Company, Lynn, Massachusetts.

EARLY USES OF NICKEL

The Accidental Element in Research

Before nickel in alloy steel was an established fact, it was introduced in a rather unusual manner.

In the early eighties a paper on possible uses of nickel steel for naval ordnance was read in London and found its way to Washington. At that time there was a bad yellow fever epidemic in New Orleans. Attempts to stamp out the disease by known methods proved ineffectual. Someone suggested that, as the yellow fever germ could not live at a low temperature, the epidemic might be stopped by isolating the patients and keeping them at a sufficiently low temperature. A hospital ship equipped with refrigerating apparatus, moored in the Mississippi River, was the plan decided upon.

Some studies of refrigerating machinery showed that one of the difficulties was to get a metal which would withstand the corrosive action of ammonia gas. The committee of Congress which had the matter in charge decided that the new alloy known as nickel-steel was the best metal. Thereupon bids were sent out for nickel. It was found that the world supply of nickel, which up to that time had been used principally for coinage, was so limited that some new supply would have to be found to meet the demand for this hospital ship.

Colonel R. M. Thompson, at that time proprietor of the Orford Copper Company, had on his hands a so-called copper ore, from the Sudbury district of Canada, which he found contained a substantial amount of nickel. There were no known methods about 1880 for separating nickel from copper as found in these ores.   Here was an ore which contained the nickel the Government wanted for the hospital ship, but no way to get it out.   Having, however, the courage of his convictions, Colonel Thompson went to Washington and agreed to supply the nickel.

A small blast furnace, through which these ores were smelted, was tried with every known flux which could be brought to Bayonne, N. J., with no results.   Finally it was agreed that the general accumulation of miscellaneous ores, fluxes, and other materials would better be cleaned up before any further attempt was made.   In the process of cleaning up Colonel Thompson had pointed out to him by one of his superintendents a pot of metal which had separated when dumped   No serious thought was given to this incident, but it was sufficiently suggestive to lead to sampling.   The result showed the nickel in the bottom and the copper in the top.

The question then was, Which and what of the ingredients put through the blast furnace, in the process of cleaning up, were responsible for the result?

By a process of elimination the proper combination was established.   This separating process was known from that time on as the "Orford Process."

This Narrative was contributed by Mr. A. J. Wadhams, Assistant General Superintendent, The International Nickel Company, Bayonne, New Jersey.

AN AMMONIA GAS STORY

A Simple Solution of a Safety Problem

Research does not always involve tedious experimentation. When helpful knowledge of former research is available, and men coöperate, problems are sometimes quickly solved. Necessity for research often arises in the ordinary practice of engineering. The solution of a problem for one purpose may be useful in many others, if properly recorded. But records to be useful must be accessible. The technical and scientific societies and journals and our libraries can be helpful, if utilized; also the Research Information Service of the National Research Council.

Ammonia in some forms is, with impunity, used daily for many household purposes, but ammonia gas in quantity is deadly. Nevertheless, this gas is extensively employed for refrigerating and other processes. It may be safely used, if rightly controlled. Some years ago many fatal accidents occurred due to safety valves on ammonia pipes discharging the gas into the operating rooms of refrigerating plants, hotels and manufacturing establishments. As a consequence, Massachusetts and New York passed laws requiring safety valves to have a discharge pipe through the roof of the building, the pipe to extend ten feet above the roof, if the adjoining building were higher.

In New York state one of the first problems encountered under the new law was the piping in the sixty-storied Woolworth Building on lower Broadway, New York City. There were but few data available by which the size of the ammonia

16

discharge pipe could be figured, because little was known about the difference of pressure required to put a given quantity of super-heated ammonia gas through a long pipe, the pipe being open to the air at one end. Experiments were then made to deduce a formula for the flow of ammonia gas in a pipe open to the air. What quantity would flow through a pipe of given length and diameter, under a given pressure at the entrance end of the pipe? Similar experiments were made on the discharge of steam. From these data it became evident that a 2-inch safety valve had to have a 6-inch pipe to discharge, even with 5 pounds pressure above the atmosphere at the entrance of the pipe, the quantity of ammonia gas that would pass through the 2-inch safety valve.

The old idea then came into the minds of two engineers working on the problem, that the flow of steam from 275 pounds absolute pressure into the air was practically the same in quantity as the flow of steam at 275 pounds absolute pressure into a chamber where the pressure was 150 pounds absolute. This led to the design of an ammonia safety valve discharging against back pressure. The question was: What was the upper limit of back pressure that an ammonia valve could discharge against?

Other series of tests were made to determine this minimum pressure. It was found that the flow into a reservoir where the back pressure was 0.585 times the entrance pressure (that is, somewhat more than half the entrance pressure) was exactly the same as the flow into a reservoir where the pressure was atmospheric. As a result, a safety valve was designed which would discharge against back pressure. Tests on this valve showed that the theory was correct. Ammonia safety valves as built to-day are made in such a way that they are capable of discharging against this high back pressure.

This, of course, means that the discharge pipe in cases like that mentioned, instead of being six inches in diameter, can be of a very much smaller size, since the entrance pressure in this pipe is now approximately 150 pounds instead of five pounds above the atmosphere. The resulting economy and convenience are obvious, as well as the satisfactory solution of this detail problem in the safe use of ammonia gas.

Information for this Narrative was furnished by Professor Edward F. Miller, Massachusetts Institute of Technology, Cambridge.

MAKING EXPLOSIONS BENEFICIAL

Research as a Sociological Factor

Both physical and social eruptions occurring suddenly and with violence are "explosions." Commonly the word suggests uncontrolled action with disastrous consequences. Many kinds of physical explosions have been brought so thoroughly under control by science, that they are utilized continually in commerce, in industry and in sport,—for quarrying and tunneling, for internal combustion engines, and for firearms,—not to mention war. Science has not yet brought social explosions under control, nor made their energy beneficial. Research in social energy is repeatedly suggested to Engineering Foundation.

"The engineer who surveys the social structure finds that certain recognized laws of evolution by which species of plants and animals come into being, grow, prosper, decline, or become extinct, are equally applicable to mankind, not merely in the abstract and in the remote past, but in the United States, in 1921. We are witnessing acute, rapid action of these laws, but it has attracted little effective attention, because engineers and business executives have been too busy, and have considered these matters no affair of theirs. The public, who are people not of science but of precedent, have tried to explain the social transformation by the theory that man is a free, individual agent, that mental or social action is but loosely associated with industry, and that the discontent and uprising of classes and nations are merely annoying manifestations of general perversity, which can best be cured by ethics, force of arms or imprisonment. They witness effects and draw no conclusions as to causes. They merely try to suppress effects.

"In the engineering world, disagreeable or disastrous effects serve as warnings. They call attention to forces which must either be eliminated

19

or diverted to useful work, and they incite study and investigation by the engineers, to disclose the causes of the phenomena. When these are found and understood, they often prove revolutionary in the benefits derived from them, when rightly used.

"In the earliest days of the kerosene lamp, there were many explosions, due to gasoline, which the imperfect distillation processes of that time left in the kerosene. To prevent these explosions the oil was more carefully rectified. Huge volumes of gasoline accumulated, for which there were few minor uses. But some engineering genius, remembering the force generated by the explosion of an old-style kerosene lamp, which blew husband and wife into the street—the first time they had been out together in over two years, as she testified—set to work and applied the newly discovered domestic power to the gasoline engine. One result was the automobile, now the fifth American industry."

Mr. Jordan's achievements in chemical research give weight to his suggestion. Social research must include psychiatry, which in industrial application is probably almost unknown to leaders of manufacturing and commercial corporations. Under the title "Mental Hygiene of Industry," Engineering Foundation supported Dr. E. E. Southard in a limited research in this field, which was stopped in the initial stages by his sudden death in February, 1920. The Foundation coöperated also, with National Research Council in the recent establishment of the Personnel Research Federation. American Engineering Council, under the leadership of Herbert Hoover, its President, is studying the waste resulting from lack of solution of personnel problems,—waste due to strikes, intermittent employment and unemployment.

Social explosions, like physical explosions, are of various magnitudes. Some affect only small units of a working force, others shake our greatest nations. Their causes are various; some of these causes may be discovered and disasters prevented. The energy which is manifested in social explosions may in some measure be controlled "for the good of mankind," as has the energy of gasoline and nitro-glycerine.

The quotation is from an unpublished paper on "Social Engineering," by H. W. Jordan, Research Chemist, Semet-Solvay Company, Syracuse, New York.

THE RUGGLES ORIENTATOR

A DEVICE FOR GROUND TRAINING OF AVIATORS

On January 19, 1918, W. Guy Ruggles presented to the Naval Consulting Board a device for the training of aviators in the sense of equilibration. From the time an aeroplane leaves the earth until it returns to the earth, it is sustained by a mobile medium and is capable of motion in every conceivable direction. Therefore, the piloting of an aeroplane involves a problem in physiology somewhat different from the customary activities of man while on earth.

Just what the man in a falling, spinning aeroplane might be called upon to do in his efforts to recover a normal flying position became more intricate as the problem was studied. Ruggles became convinced that the semicircular canal system of the inner ear, generally referred to as the static labyrinth, played a very important part in functioning those muscles which a pilot uses in guiding his aeroplane. This was substantiated by careful perusal of the work and experiments of famous otologists.

These scientists, by delicate surgical operations, established the fact that an animal whose semicircular canals had been removed was unable to direct its movements intelligently; and, furthermore, that while animals so operated upon might in time learn to direct their movements intelligently on the ground, they could not while in space. Spinning dancers and skaters, by practice, rotate with considerable velocity without noticeable dizziness, and trained acrobats perform feats of equilibrium totally impossible in the early stages of training.

Ruggles believed that if means were available, the student aviator might so develop his faculties of equilibration and muscular control that the piloting of an aeroplane might be mastered with a minimum of danger. The static labyrinth, being an entirely involuntary organ, operating through the involuntary system, when under the excitation of unaccustomed spinning motions and unusual positions, until more completely developed and trained, causes involuntary muscular actions entirely beyond control.

As built, the apparatus was an amplified gimbal. It had a rectangular frame in which a tubular steel ring about 9 feet in diameter rotated about a vertical axis. Within this a smaller ring was mounted for rotation about a horizontal axis, and within this a still smaller ring for rotation about an axis at right angles to either of the others. Within this third ring was a section of the fuselage of an aeroplane for the student aviator, consisting of a seat and control members. By this arrangement it was possible by the movement of the foot bar and the joy stick to operate the motors, so that the student aviator would be given a turning motion in any of the three planes of direction. In addition there was provision for a falling motion in the vertical plane. Progressive motion was not incorporated on account of the fact that human faculties do not sense a uniform motion. The falling motion, however, was of vital importance, for the labyrinth contains as a part of its mechanism six small otoliths, which sense the acceleration in the beginning of each falling motion and are responsible for the most violent muscular reactions of the involuntary system.

Rotational possibilities were made to include rates from a very few turns a minute to a maximum of thirty. While this maximum would be faster than the rotational possibilities of an aeroplane in ordinary maneuvers, it had been proved that the static labyrinth of the ear becomes accustomed to a rapid turning movement and is never affected by a movement slower than the one to which it has become accustomed. A control station was also established outside the apparatus by means of which the instructor might take the control away from the man inside and operate any or all of the motors to rotate the student.

The length of time to develop the Ruggles device may be taken as an indication of that required to develop devices in war time. It was not ready for inspection before July, 1918, so that if an inventor is given a reasonable time to develop a device before he presents it to the Government, of, say, six months, and it takes six months under war conditions to get out a full-sized working model, it can be readily understood why so many devices were just about ready to be used at the time of the armistice, November 11, 1918, war having been declared April 6, 1917.

The claims made in regard to the advantage that could be gained from training aviators on the ground before they took their first flight seemed to be borne out by tests on student aviators by the Massachusetts Institute of Technology, in Boston, Mass. The flying records of men who had been trained in the Ruggles orientator seemed to show that men who operated the orientator successfully were more likely to become aces in aviation.

By Lloyd N. Scott, formerly Liaison Officer to Naval Consulting Board and Secretary of War Committee of Technical Societies.

THE CENTRIFUGAL CREAMER

From Laboratory to Factory and Farm

In 1876 while teaching in the Central High School of Philadelphia, Professor Thomson had been using before his classes the whirling machines and models, common in cabinets of philosophical apparatus for illustrating "the central forces." He had been telling his classes of the applications in the steam engine governor, centrifugal drying machines used in laundries, and the centrifugal draining machines used in sugar refineries. While whirling a vessel containing a liquid in which there was a sediment, he was struck with the promptness with which the sediment settled to the outside of the vessel, and it occurred to him that the applications of the phenomena of centrifugal force might be considerably extended, as in the clearing of clayey or muddy liquids, or liquids having materials in suspension; the separation of fluids of different densities, especially the removal of cream from milk, which, of course, was carried out on a large scale by other methods. With Professor E. J. Houston, who assisted, it was believed that if a continuously operating machine could be devised for separation, especially of cream from milk, a notable step in advance would be made. Such a machine would involve the feeding in of the milk while the machine was kept at high speed, and the delivery of cream and the skimmed milk from separate outlets.

Experiments were carried on energetically with special apparatus. During these experiments the form of centrifuge now so common in physiological laboratories, for the separation of bacteria from cultures and for other concentrations, was invented. It consisted of an upright shaft revolving at high speed with a cross-head to which was slung by joints receivers for vessels containing the materials to be treated, generally a liquid. When the machine was at rest these vessels hung upright, but when revolving they separated, and finally stood out at high speeds in a practically horizontal plane. Numerous experiments with different substances were made with this apparatus, and the extreme celerity of separation was noted. Attempts were even made to concentrate dense solutions of salts, but without any special result. This type of apparatus found application through a friend of the inventor to the concentration of photographic emulsions, this friend being a manufacturer of photographic materials.

The development of this type of centrifuge was, however, incidental only to the further and greater application for cream separation. In the meantime inventions which had before then been made in this particular field were looked up carefully; but no example was found of any such machine having been produced, which could be kept running at steady speed, receive a stream of liquid, such as milk, and deliver the streams of separated materials, such as cream and skimmed milk. When the inventor's ideas were sufficiently crystallized they were made the subject of an application for patent, which finally issued, after a contest in the Patent Office, under the title "Centrifugal Creamer," dated April 5, 1881. One of the contestants in the Patent Office was the famous engineer, De Laval, who had before this period developed and patented an intermittent type of centrifugal creamer, in which the machine was stopped between charges and the charge removed before the reception of another. De Laval apparently made the same invention independently later, and in applying for patent found that Thomson & Houston were ahead. This resulted in his conceding priority to these inventors, and a combination of interests soon followed which led to the production and exploitation on a large scale of the earliest types of centrifugal separators used in creameries. Naturally the business grew, and the centrifugal type of creamer became essential to every dairy or creamery.

The immediate suggestion of this valuable invention came from teaching and laboratory research which had been undertaken to extend the knowledge of centrifugal action. This, coupled with close observation and an understanding of the needs of the arts and industries, is what often leads to important advances.

This Narrative was contributed by Dr. Elihu Thomson, Consulting Engineer, General Electric Company, Lynn, Massachusetts.

NITROGEN

Its Capture and Utilization

That nitrogen compounds are essential to human life, and that nitrogen gas constitutes four-fifths of the atmosphere of our planet, are items of common knowledge. For fertilizers, for explosives, for food, for dyes, for innumerable necessaries, modern industry demands nitrogen compounds in huge quantities. Because of the abundance of nitrogen in the air and the relative scarcity of usable compounds in the earth, many have been the endeavors to obtain nitrogen or its compounds directly from the atmosphere. The difficulties are great, but research has produced more than one successful method. One of the well-known processes bears the name of Haber, a German chemist, who achieved it by patient and expensive research along lines scientifically indicated, making ammonia as an intermediate product.

In 1785 Cavendish observed and recorded the production of nitric acid on the passage of an electric spark through the air, and through the work of Bradley at Niagara Falls this led directly to methods for the fixation of atmospheric nitrogen.

It had been observed that at atmospheric pressure, the quantity of ammonia formed by the combination of nitrogen and hydrogen gases was extremely small, even at a temperature believed to be requisite for rapid reaction between the two gases. At higher temperatures still less ammonia formed. Theoretically, quantities of ammonia vastly larger should be formed if the gases could be subjected to great pressure as well as high temperature during the reaction. But these gases have so little inclination to become intimate that a real provocation is needed to get them together. A "teaser" is used for this purpose, which the chemists for lack of a better name call a catalyst. A catalyst takes good care to see that it does not itself get involved in the reaction which it starts. The catalyst chosen for this case was the rare metal, uranium.

The hydrogen needed in Haber's process is obtained by decomposing water, which in the form of steam is forced into a furnace containing red hot coke; the nitrogen is gotten from liquid air.

Germany simply had to have an unlimited source of nitrogen supply within her own borders as an industrial safeguard, as well as a military necessity, before she could start a great war. Haber was backed by one of the powerful and wealthy German chemical corporations. For years his research went on, seeking practical methods and developing apparatus of industrially adequate capacity. Many millions of marks were spent, but the result was of priceless value.

Nearly twenty years ago, Thomas A. Edison was experimenting with the reduction of iron by hydrogen for his storage battery. During these experiments, he observed that a large quantity of ammonia developed, but gave this occurrence no special thought; the ammonia simply was troublesome. Lloyd N. Scott, formerly Liaison Officer to the Naval Consulting Board, records that in May, 1917, when Mr. Edison was President of the Naval Consulting Board, and when our country was searching for a process for obtaining nitrogen for war uses, Mr. Edison recalled his previous experiments and thought that some use might be made of the production of ammonia in that way.   Mr. Edison then set up his old apparatus and found that by mixing lampblack with the reduced iron the passage of nitrogen and hydrogen over the mixture produced ammonia continuously in large quantity and at low pressure.

Other processes have been invented by Americans.

Based on information from various sources.

LIGHT IN WATER

TOTAL REFLECTION BY ANIMALCULES

It is natural to suppose that light penetrates clear water as it does glass. The Prince of Monaco, one of the greatest students of marine life, has shown, however, that there are myriads of animalcules in sea-water and that they cause almost total reflection of a beam of light projected into the water. Therefore, water is not like glass in its transmission of light.

In connection with submarine detection studies, Mr. Elmer A. Sperry, member of the Naval Consulting Board, made some elaborate experiments on projecting light through water, from which instructive results were obtained. An electric light was used having a sixty million candle-power beam, which could be seen through air for 62 miles (150 amperes, 75 volts, condensed and directed by a 36-inch projector).

This light was placed in the bottom of a steel well resembling a boiler 25 feet long, with an opening in its side near the bottom 40 inches in diameter, in which a plate-glass window one inch thick was sealed. There were several tons of lead in the bottom of the well so that it would sink vertically to any desired depth. It was hung by a bale from a crane on a large barge.

The light was first tested in the muddy waters of the New York Navy Yard, at a depth of 10 or 15 feet below the surface. There was a total reflection of light, but this was attributed at that time to the great muddiness of the water.

A luminescent sphere approximately 80 feet in diameter surrounded the window. This luminescence was wonderfully brilliant and acted like a fog to obscure vision. Brilliancy of luminescence seemed to be about the same at all points of the sphere, even exactly back of the well in the rear of the window through which the light was projected.

Experiments were then made in clear ocean water near the easterly end of Long Island. Here also it was found that the beam of light could not be projected through the water as had been hoped, and that a globe of luminescence was produced as in the experiments in the New York Navy Yard. The globe of luminescence was visible through this comparatively clear water for possibly a quarter of a mile, and it could be used for the purpose of silhouetting mines, anchors, cables and other objects of this nature, against its white background with very great distinctness, up to this distance of a quarter of a mile.

The results of these interesting experiments with so powerful a light are a real contribution to our knowledge of the art of projecting light through water. They indicate the impracticability, in most situations, of projecting light to any great depth into water in such a way as to be an aid to divers employed on ordinary under-water operations, or for other purposes.

Based upon information from Lloyd N. Scott, formerly Liaison Officer to Naval Consulting Board, and Secretary of War Committee of Technical Societies.

THERMIONICS

The Movement of Electricity Under Influence of High Temperature in Vacua

Effective illustrations of the immense value of research are found in the application of the work of a few University laboratories in the development of thermionic discharge and the laws governing it to the problems of telegraphy, telephony, rectification of currents and radiology. The commercial values involved represent at present unquestionably hundreds of millions of dollars, and yet for at least ten years this field was developed exclusively by research men in university laboratories with no immediate motive other than the discovering of the laws of nature. R. A. Millikan, Professor of Physics, University of Chicago. (1924, California Institute of Technology.)

Although thermionics is the latest branch of electrical science to be adapted to the service of man, its history dates back two hundred years.

In 1725, nearly one hundred years before the discovery of the phenomena of electromagnetism which form the basis of most modern electrical developments, DuFay discovered that the space in the neighborhood of a red hot body is a conductor of electricity. In 1887, Elster and Geitel found that an electric charge can be made to pass through vacuo from a hot body to another body in its vicinity. This phenomenon had been observed by Edison in 1884, who noticed that a discharge passed between the positive and negative ends of the filament in an incandescent lamp. It was not, however, until

1902 that the laws of thermionics were worked out by Richardson who examined the current flowing between a heated filament and a surrounding cylinder. The experiments were carried out in a high vacuum and the variation of the current with the temperature of the filament was determined. It was found that the phenomena observed could be quantitatively explained on the assumption that free electrons, or small particles of negative electricity, are boiled off from the heated metal.

In recent years a number of valuable devices have been invented which depend for their action on the passage of an electric current between a hot and a cold electrode in an evacuated vessel.

In the thermionic rectifier one of the electrodes is a filament which can be heated by an auxiliary current and the other is a metal plate. These electrodes are sealed into a glass bulb which is exhausted to a high vacuum. Since the electrons emitted by the filament are charged negatively, current can pass through the tube in one direction only and the device acts as a rectifier of alternating currents. When used for the rectification of signaling currents, as, for example, the weak currents received by a wireless antenna, it is known as a "detector," and was first used for this purpose by Fleming in 1905. Thermionic rectifiers readily lend themselves to the rectification of high voltage currents, and the General Electric Company has made tubes capable of rectifying 250 milliamperes at 100,000 volts.

In a modified form known as the "Tungar rectifier" the current in the tube is increased by the admission of argon into the bulb. In the case of the tubes designed to handle small power, the electrode which serves as a primary source of electrons is heated by an auxiliary current; but in the case of the larger power tubes the auxiliary current is turned off after the tube gets into operation, the hot electrode from then on being heated from the effects of the gaseous discharge.

The electrons emitted by a hot cathode have also been utilized in the Coolidge X-ray tube. X-rays are formed when electrons moving at high speeds impinge on matter. In the older forms of X-ray tubes the electrons are obtained from the electrical discharge through the residual gas. The variability of the gas content of the tube and the fact that the electrons are formed at all parts of the tube make it impossible to obtain as uniform results as with the Coolidge tube, in which very high vacua are used, the electrons being obtained from a heated cathode. The use of these tubes has very greatly increased the precision of the X-ray art.

In 1907, DeForest discovered that the current between the hot and cold elements in a vacuum tube could be influenced by varying the potential of a third electrode placed in the tube. It was shown by him that with the proper special arrangement very small potentials applied to the third electrode were capable of producing comparatively large changes in the current flowing through the tube. This device De Forest proposed as a wireless detector, and he named it the "audion." It is primarily an amplifier of electrical currents, and consequently can also be used as a generator of alternating currents when connected in suitable circuits. During the war it came to be the basic element in wireless communication and was made in very large quantities.

In this country the development of the audion into a reliable structure has been largely due to the research departments of the Bell Telephone System and of the General Electric Company. The engineers of the Bell Telephone System have reduced it to a precision instrument for wire telephony, and it is a basic factor in commercial long distance telephony. By its use, carrier current multiplex wire telephony and telegraphy have been accomplished, and it is now commercially possible to transmit a number of telephone and telegraph messages over the same pair of wires at the same time.

Contributed by Dr. W. Wilson, of the Western Electric Company, Inc., New York.

RADIOACTIVITY

New Conceptions of the Constitution of Matter

In 1895, Röntgen discovered X-rays and pushed ajar a door into a new realm of science. The very name indicates lack of knowledge, but X-rays have made a place for themselves in the daily experiences of all civilized peoples. Röntgen, in his public announcement January 6, 1896, made the world aware of radiations which could penetrate bodies opaque to light, and after such penetration, or before, could affect photographic plates, or films, in the same manner as light This discovery stimulated search for other manifestations of this wonderful property of matter.

Among these searchers was M. Henri Becquerel, a French scientist. He was looking for something and found a great deal more. Again the "accidental" in research! While studying phosphorescence, he covered a photographic plate with black paper and on it put a small amount of a compound of uranium. His choice of uranium was as fortunate as Mendel's selection of hawkweed for experiments in heredity was unfortunate. After exposure of the phosphorescent uranium compound to sunlight, and subsequent development of the plate, it was found that rays from the uranium had penetrated the paper and affected the plate, although the sunlight had not. Thin sheets of metal also could be pierced, as was revealed by trial with additional photographic plates. The sun's action on the phosphorescent body was believed necessary. One day, however, clouds obscured the sun, interrupting an experiment. The wrapped plate, with uranium compound lying on it, was laid away in a dark place. Weeks afterwards Becquerel developed this plate and found that it had been affected just as the plates in the earlier tests had been. What did it? Additional tests eliminated sunlight and phosphorescence, and proved that a hitherto unrecognized property resided in uranium. By use of an uranium compound, Becquerel made a print of an aluminum medal, bringing out in clear relief the human head stamped thereon. Thus was radioactivity discovered in 1896. Were there other substances than uranium radio-active? The search went on. Soon the Curies discovered polonium, then radium in 1898, and their associate, Debierne, found actinium also in pitch-blende, the mineral which is one of the chief sources of radium. In subsequent years, thorium and its disintegration product mesothorium, and other radioactive substances and minerals from which they could be obtained were found. These discoveries put new aspects upon matter and its constitution. Fundamental, fresh conceptions were introduced into physical science.

From the delicate, complex apparatus of the modern physical laboratory, the involved processes of research with their exacting refinements, and the abstruse mathematical computations, most technologists turn in despair. Such things are too time-consuming, and too "impracticable" for them. Nevertheless, from these researches in pure science in pursuit of knowledge of radioactivity, there came results of vast importance, extremely practical in peace and war.

No one could have foreseen the possibility that the in-finitesimal traces of the previously unknown element radium, found in the most forlorn quarters of the earth, would in a few years be turned into a practical tool for therapy and be used almost entirely for cancer treatment. It could hardly have been foreseen that the wrist watches of the soldiers in the trenches of a world war would have called for some of this radium, nor could anyone have imagined that this call would have resulted, through other pure research, in the disclosure of mesothorium now sold throughout the world at an enormous price, to take the place of radium in the illuminated watch or an airplane compass dial. From that pure scientific study, markets expressed in millions of dollars quickly resulted.

A large life insurance company, as a business proposition, not long ago contributed $30,000 for aiding the application of radium to the treatment of cancer, solely because it had found that to increase the longevity of cancer patients insured with it, by radium treatment, was to its advantage.

Doubtless, there are just as remarkable, unexpected, and interesting cases yet to be developed. There is, however, no short cut. Somebody has had to sweat mentally and physically to bring such things into existence.

Prepared with assistance of Dr. Willis R. Whitney, Director, Research Laboratory, General Electric Company, and lectures by Prof. Frederick Soddy on "The Interpretation of Radium and the Structure of the Atom."

WROUGHT TUNGSTEN

A REWARD OF MANY YEARS SPENT IN SCIENTIFIC RESEARCH

The "impossible" is the thing we have not yet learned how to do.

Until 1904, tungsten had been known for a century and a quarter only in its unrefined state. Its value as a hardening alloy had, it is true, been recognized and appreciated. In 1905 and thereafter the metal, mixed with paste and squirted through dies, had given the incandescent lamp its most efficient filament; but the brittleness of this filament caused great embarrassment to electric lamp makers and users alike.

For many years Dr. W. D. Coolidge, of the Research Laboratory of the General Electric Company, had sought a process for making tungsten ductile. The feat was regarded as almost impossible by metallurgists. To make any ordinary metal soft, it is heated to a temperature above its annealing point and then cooled to room temperature. This process, however, left tungsten as brittle as ever.

It was eventually found that the only way to make the metal ductile was to mash the grains out into fibrosity and thus make it ductile while cold. This was accomplished by first heating the tungsten to a temperature below its annealing point and then mechanically working it with infinite care at a variety of degrees of heat, each less than the one preceding it, until it was at room temperature. A similar treatment would, if applied to ordinary metals, destroy their ductility.

A process was worked out which, if followed without the slightest deviation, stretched the grains out and the metal was made ductile; but if the working varied from this process, failure resulted. The tungsten would break at a stroke, when cold.

Thus, after years of patient labor a triumph of far-reaching consequence in the field of research was rewarded. The filament produced had a startling tensile strength—about 600,000 pounds per square inch for wire one-thousandth of an inch in diameter. It was so pliable that it could be wound into any form safely and handled with no thought of its breaking.

Wolframite is the most important tungsten ore. It is obtained from both Korea and the United States. Extraction from the ore is comparatively simple, yielding metallic tungsten in the form of powder of various density. This powder is formed into ingots by great hydraulic pressure—not by fusion. The melting point of tungsten is about 3350°C., being higher than for any other known metal. From ingots to fine wire there are many steps, every one important, in the complicated process.

The tungsten filament has doubled the efficiency of incandescent lamps and provides a white light of far purer quality than any lamp heretofore known. It has provided new targets for X-ray tubes, phonograph needles fifty times as efficient as any that preceded them, better ignition contacts for automobiles, and many other new articles and improvements of old ones.

Trained facilities for scientific study and experiment, a spirit of indomitable perseverance, and the facilities afforded by a completely equipped laboratory made this achievement possible.

The story of ductile tungsten is one of the romances of research—the epic of accomplishing the "impossible."

"The manufacture of tungsten and tungsten products is a chemical engineering process that requires very careful manipulation with hydrogen under dangerous conditions. Many important mechanical and electrical, as well as chemical operations are involved. A high degree of ingenuity in the design and operation of special apparatus is required. It is a striking example of progress in the development of our chemical industries."—*The Chemical Bulletin*, February, 1920.

Contributed by Dr. Irving Langmuir, Research Laboratory, General Electric Company, Schenectady, New York.

THE GAS FILLED INCANDESCENT LAMP

A Product of Continued Search for Higher Efficiency

Since 1879, when Edison gave the world the incandescent lamp, men have been working to improve this carbon filament vacuum light. A better filament was desired. Research produced tungsten filaments, and the name of a metal so rare as to be almost a curiosity became a household word.

The use of tungsten as a filament did not solve all the lamp manufacturers' problems, although some electrical men held that with the development of wrought tungsten by Dr. W. D. Coolidge, of the General Electric Company, lamp development had gone its limit. However, the lamp was far from perfect. A further reduction in the consumption of current was still desired and bulb blackening, which began as soon as the current was turned on, impaired the lamp's lighting power. All sorts of remedies were tried with little success.

Scientists in the research laboratory at Schenectady undertook a number of fundamental investigations and it was not until three-fourths of the preliminary work had been done on a purely scientific basis that the real commercial usefulness of the results became apparent.

Brittleness of the filament having been overcome by the development of wrought tungsten, the necessity for preventing bulb blackening still remained.

Investigations along the lines of better vacua in lamps showed it was impracticable to determine whether variations in method or amount of exhaustion caused improvement.

So studies were made along two lines: 1. The sources of gas within a lamp; 2. The effects produced in lamps by various gases.

Research showed that the small amounts of water vapor present in the bulb greatly hastened blackening. The vapor oxidized the tungsten, freeing hydrogen in the atomic state. The oxide went to the bulb and was there reduced to metallic tungsten by the active hydrogen, releasing the oxygen which reunited with the hydrogen to form water. Thus the vicious cycle recurred until the lamp's life was ended.

Early experimenters, Edison among them, had made numerous trials of a gas-filled bulb but in every case the experimental gas-filled lamp was decidedly inferior to the vacuum carbon lamp then in use. However, experiments showed that if a tungsten filament were heated close to its melting point in a gas-filled bulb entirely freed from water vapor, the filament lasted much longer than when heated in a vacuum, and the heavier the gas used, the more the evaporation of the metal was retarded. But the addition of the gas to increase the life of the filament meant an additional heat loss.

It was found, however, that the presence of a dense gas, such as nitrogen or the hitherto unused argon, in the bulb, reduced the rate of filament evaporation to about one per cent of what it was in a vacuum at the same temperature. The convection currents in the gas carried the deposit of tungsten nitride to the top of the lamp, where it interfered little with the lamp's lighting powers.

By using a large filament, or a coil of small filament, the heat loss was overcome by the higher temperature, and better, whiter light was produced.

Thus, through careful and exhaustive research we have today a lamp whose gleam far outshines the rather feeble glow of the early incandescent light, and the old lamp is a thing of the past.

Contributed by Dr. Irving Langmuir, Research Laboratory, General Electric Company, Schenectady, New York.

RADIUM

A Substance so Powerful that One Three-Thousand-Millionth of a Grain Can Be Identified Easily

On account of Madame Curie's recent visit, radium and radioactivity have acquired a new interest. Radium is found only in uranium ores. Uranium is the "mother" of radium; radium is formed from uranium by disintegration, through a series of atomic changes. Radium also disintegrates and ultimately forms lead as the final product of the uranium series. Each radioactive element has a definite rate at which the change takes place; some are extremely slow, some rapid. It takes about five billion years for one-half a given quantity of uranium to change into other products. Radium A, one of the disintegration products, requires only 3.05 minutes, while one-half of any given amount of radium changes in 1690 years. Those rates of change are definite and fixed, and up to the present, no means, either physical or chemical, have been discovered which can either retard or accelerate the disintegration rate of any radioactive element.

During these atomic changes, three types of rays are given out. The alpha particle is atomic in mass, and in fact is a helium atom with two positive charges on it. It has a velocity of from 8,000 to 12,000 miles a second, but owing to its relatively large mass, it does not penetrate matter to any great extent. A thin sheet of writing paper will stop alpha particles, and their range in air is only a few centimeters.

46

The beta rays consist of negatively charged electrons similar to the cathode rays in a Crookes' tube. Their velocity varies from about 100,000 miles a second up to nearly that of light, 186,000 miles a second. The mass of the beta particle is about 1/1600 that of a hydrogen atom; it represents the negative particles out of which all matter is built up.

The third ray given out in radioactive changes, the gamma ray, is very similar to X-rays. Both are vibrations in the ether of very short wave length, but the gamma ray has a much shorter wave length than the X-ray, and is much more penetrating. It is the gamma ray which is almost exclusively used in treating cancer by means of radium, the alpha and beta rays being screened off by one or two millimeters of lead, through which the gamma rays can penetrate.

Any element, therefore, is radioactive which spontaneously gives rise to changes of one element into another with the elimination of alpha, beta, or gamma rays.

For many years radium was exclusively produced from the Austrian ores at Joachimsthal. Later, radium was obtained from pitchblende deposits in Cornwall, and from autenite deposits in Portugal. About nine years ago, officials of the Bureau of Mines found that the carnotite deposits in southwestern Colorado and eastern Utah represented the largest bodies of radium-bearing ore in the world. At the present time, the United States produces much more radium than all the rest of the world together.

From the beginning of the industry in 1913 to January, 1921, approximately 115 grams of radium element have been produced in this country. Probably not more than 40 grams have been recovered from foreign ores since the discovery of radium by Madame Curie. This industry has assumed an exceedingly great importance owing to the therapeutic use for radium. Cancer is being continually cured by the use of radium. All cancer, however, cannot be so cured, and it requires a skilled surgeon who thoroughly understands the proper dosage in order to get favorable results.

A NEW THEORY OF RADIOACTIVITY

Beyond the gamma rays there may exist rays of light much more penetrating, which it is possible to conceive of as producing the phenomena of radioactivity. Madame Curie has proved that these rays cannot proceed from the Sun. It is quite possible that this active radiation issues from beneath our very feet, from the hardened center of the planet itself, that the earth is constantly emitting ultra-X-rays, which are so much more penetrating than either X-rays or gamma rays, as to be able to traverse a thick layer of rocks, and that these ultra-X-rays produce various forms of observed radioactivity.—Jean Perrin, *Scientific American Monthly*, August, 1921.

Contributed by R. B. Moore, Chief Chemist, Bureau of Mines, and published by permission of the Director of the Bureau.

HELIUM

One of the Rare Gases of the Atmosphere-Helium, Neon, Argon, Krypton and Xenon

Helium is in the air in the proportion of one part in 185,000 by volume; neon, one part in 60,000; argon, one part in 104; krypton, one part in 19 million, and xenon, one part in 190 million. These gases are all inert, do not react with other elements, and for this reason probably more than for any other, they have excited great interest among chemists. Next to hydrogen helium is the lightest gas known, having twice the density of hydrogen.

Helium has been liquefied by Professor Onnes in Leyden. The liquid boils at $-268.75°C$, which is very close to absolute zero, that is, $-273°C$. Onnes is the only one who has liquefied helium, and he used the small amount of liquid obtained to determine some of the properties of matter at this extremely low temperature. What has been done is significant enough to make it very desirable to have liquid helium in quantity so that further experimental work along this line may be carried out.

Helium is found in the gases of many mineral springs. It is also found in natural gas in a large number of localities in the United States, particularly in Texas, Oklahoma, Kansas and Ohio. About four hundred million cubic feet of helium is going to waste each year from this source alone.

Since helium is not inflammable and has 92 per cent. of the lifting power of hydrogen, during the war, it became of great military value. The plan was to substitute helium for hydrogen in balloons and dirigibles, and thus make it impossible to bring these vessels to earth by means of incendiary bullets. Such a change would make tremendous progress in aeronautics, for both commercial and war purposes.

With this object in view, the U. S. Government has experimented on the extraction of helium from natural gas in Texas, and during the war three experimental plants were built and operated. At present one of these experimental plants is still being operated and a large production plant has been constructed at Fort Worth. It is hoped that the Government will support these plants on account of the fact that the United States is the only country in the world at the present time which has sufficient helium in its natural gas for war and commercial purposes.

The origin of helium in natural gas is uncertain. During radioactive changes, helium is thrown off in the form of the alpha particle, which is a helium atom with two positive charges. However, we are not acquainted with sufficient supplies of uranium or thorium ores to account for the large volumes of helium present in natural gas in this country.

If the helium does not come from radioactive changes, it might have come from the sun, if the earth was really thrown off from the sun. The chromosphere, or surrounding envelope of the sun, consists of incandescent hydrogen and helium. It is possible that the viscous mass of the earth in passing through the sun's atmosphere picked up sufficient gas to account for the helium now found below the earth's crust.

The price of helium before the war was approximately $2000 a cubic foot. It is believed that in the new plant at Fort Worth helium may be produced for a little less than 6 cents a cubic foot.

DISCOVERY OF HELIUM

Janssen, during a solar eclipse in 1868, detected new lines in the spectrum of the sun's atmosphere, but did not assign them to a new element. Sir J. Norman Lockyer also observed these lines the same year, and suggested the name "Helium" (sun element). Sir William Ramsay, in 1895, first identified helium on the earth as the principal constituent of the gaseous mixture given off on heating cleveite, a mineral found in Norway. Helium was found later in several other minerals and in the earth's atmosphere. It has so far resisted all attempts to cause it to combine with other elements. Helium is one of the products formed in radioactive changes. Onnes liquefied helium in 1908, and found it next to liquid hydrogen the lightest liquid known, specific gravity 0.122, at approximately 4 degrees absolute, or 269 degrees below zero Centigrade.

Contributed by R. B. Moore, Chief Chemist, Bureau of Mines, and published by permission of the Director of the Bureau.

DIRECTION BY TWO EARS

In 1917, the Atlantic seemed likely once more to become a barrier of separation instead of a ferry for commerce between the Americas and Europe. Shipbuilders and ship destroyers were having a thrilling race. But it was far more important to save ships; for replacement of bottoms did not compensate for loss of essential cargoes, nor for indispensable lives. Submarine detection was the problem. Once detected in good season, means of destruction could be used.

British, French and American scientists coöperated upon the problem and numerous solutions were found. Most effective among these was an American development of a French idea. Lenses of glass for concentration of light rays are familiar objects; but how many persons have seen a sound lens? Such a lens, or device for bringing incoming sound impulses together at a focal point, was the important element in the detector mentioned. In the improved device a large number of sound receivers were placed in two rows, one on each side of the keel of the ship, near the bow. The sound impulses coming into all of the receivers on one side, travelled in tubes of just such lengths as to unite in the same phase at the mount of a tube leading to one ear of the observer, while all the sound impulses received by the other row were brought together by a similar way at the other ear.

Man, like many other animals, has two ears, in order that he may the more accurately determine the directions from which sounds come. The binaural sense, unaided, can determine direction of sound within five to ten degrees. The hand of a time-piece changes its direction six degrees when it moves one minute on the dial. With the aid of the acoustical form of the detector, submarines could be heard one to ten miles away, dependent upon conditions of weather and speed, and the direction could be determined within one or two degrees.

An electrical form of detector of still greater sensitiveness is being developed for peace rather than for war, because submarines are no longer a menace, but icebergs and fogs still invade the sea lanes. Any effective means for preventing collisions in fogs, with other vessels or with bergs, could save property of great value and many lives. The avoidance of the loss of one great liner alone would be worth all the cost.

When the French official report about the detector as originally invented was secretly read to the Anti-Submarine Board, of our Navy, one of our leading physicists, Colonel Robert A. Millikan, was in the group. He took the problem of improvement to a party of scientists gathered in a hotel at the Naval Experiment Station at New London, Connecticut. For two days, ten men focused their thoughts on the subject and produced a number of modifications of the French device, one of which was so successfully developed, as described above. It may yet make the fog as little to be dreaded as was a German submarine after a depth bomb had done its work.

Prepared from information supplied by Colonel Robert A. Millikan, California Institute of Technology, Pasadena.

WHITTLING IRON

SOME IRONS ARE SOFTENED BY SALINE, ACIDULOUS AND
ALKALINE WATERS

In 1545, the *Mary Rose* capsized off Spithead, England.
She carried some wrought-iron guns and cast-iron shot.
After 292 years in the sea, on being brought into the air
the shot gradually became red hot, then fell to pieces. A
similar fate overtook the *Royal George* in 1782 in the same
locality, and 62 years later some iron guns were recovered
from the wreck. After 133 years' submergence, some cannon
and shot were brought up from the *Edgar*, also. It is recorded that the cast iron from the latter two vessels was
generally soft, so that it could be cut with a knife, resembling
plumbago. Wrought iron on these ships was not so seriously
injured. While in this soft state, some of the old cannon were
taken carefully to the Tower of London. In the Minutes of
the Proceedings of the (British) Institution of Civil Engineers,
about eight years ago, Major General Pasley records that
after a time these cannon resumed their original hardness.
The same authority declares that iron parts of pumps
immersed in mineralized waters were similarly affected.
Another authority states that the old guns mentioned were
again fired. Cast-iron piles along the English coast likewise
deteriorated.

In the Transactions of the American Society of Civil
Engineers for 1915, Marshall R. Pugh narrates that "the
cast-iron guns from some ancient pirate ship were brought
up from the ocean depths off Holyhead in 1822, after the
lapse of a century. They were quite soft, but hardened so

54

much on exposure to the air that they were used to fire salutes to King George IV when he passed through Holyhead on his way to Dublin. These old guns were said to have given louder reports than any others!"

Old sea tales might be multiplied. Modern shipbuilders, too, state that in repair work, cast-iron parts exposed to sea-water are frequently found in the condition described, at least in spots.

Iron pipes along the seaboard are so deteriorated by salt water as to need replacement, in some places, within a few years, whilst in other places a generation or even two may pass. This deterioration appears to be more rapid in tidal marsh land than in seaways. It has been learned, also, that coal ashes and certain industrial wastes deposited on the land, through leaching, cause the same unfortunate results. Likewise, pipes and other iron objects in alkaline, acid or saline soils, in many localities suffer deterioration. All kinds of iron are not affected, nor is the action uniform.

Narratives of such troubles could be written for many parts of our country and other countries. A little knowledge has been gained about this form of corrosion, and some methods for avoiding it partially have been developed. However, it is still a menace to many iron objects, jeopardizing valuable property, and, indirectly, human lives.

A more thorough investigation than has ever been undertaken is demanded. Engineering Foundation is endeavoring to organize a research that will get valuable results. Information concerning the trouble must be countered by scientific knowledge of causes and means for avoidance or resistance. Manifestly, it is undesirable to have iron in pipes or structures become soft enough to be whittled with a jack-knife and in extreme cases, as soft as putty.

Based on information from various sources.

MALEIC AND FUMARIC ACIDS

A Chemical Romance: Discovery of Catalytic Oxidation of Coal Tar Products

Eight years is a long time to seek an objective and then
find something else. Happy is the man whose disappoint-
ment is delightful! About 1912, Doctors J. M. Weiss and
C. R. Downs, in The Barrett Company's laboratories, began
the quest of direct methods for production of the highly
efficacious disinfectants, such as Pyxol. Their sources are
the acids in coal tar. But the yield from American tars was
very small as compared with Scotch blast furnace tars, because of differences in industrial processes.

As a first step toward independence of foreign supplies,
endeavor was made to produce tar acids directly by using
iron oxide as the catalyst ("chemical parson") to cause the
desired union between creosote oil and air, mixed at high
temperatures. Failures led to substitution of benzol for
creosote oil with the idea of producing the simplest tar acid,
phenol (carbolic acid). So small a quantity of phenol resulted that the process was not practical.

Then thirty to forty substances were listed for trial as
catalysts. Vanadium oxide was the third one tried. In a
short time crystals were found in the condenser tube, but
they were not phenol. Tests showed that these crystals were
maleic acid, a basic substance from which many valuable
products can be made. Benzol, a ring compound (so-called
from the shape of the chemical diagram representing its
composition), had been changed to maleic acid, a straight-

chair compound, a transmutation never before directly accomplished.

A vast new field was opened. But laborious work for several years by chemists and engineers was expended in developing practical, economical methods and apparatus for commercial manufacture. Success has been achieved. Previous to this synthetic production, probably no laboratory in the world had ever possessed a pound of maleic acid. It was derived from certain fruit juices and sold in small quantities at prices approximating those of gold and platinum. It was then a curiosity—not a base for articles of commerce.

By treating with an inexpensive acid, maleic acid is changed to fumaric acid, its isomer (chemical "twin" of opposite sex), formerly also of great rarity. From one or the other of these acids can be made cream of tartar, new drugs and dyes, malic, aspartic, lactic and other acids. Some old drugs and dyes can be cheapened by their aid.

It was also discovered that by this process of catalytic oxidation, many other chemicals could be derived directly from benzol and other coal tar ingredients.

Both maleic and fumaric acids are white crystalline solids; the former is very soluble in water, the latter almost insoluble. Benzol dissolves only a trace of either. Maleic acid solution corrodes most metals except platinum and silver. Solid dry acid, however, may be kept in metal containers. Fumaric acid has almost no taste, maleic acid has a sour, bitter, very disagreeable taste. Yet these two acids, so different in properties, are of the same chemical composition, varying only in internal structure. Mere heating changes maleic into fumaric acid.

This is another case of an unexpected result of research and an example of coöperation. The work involved many men.

Prepared from information supplied by Dr. J. M. Weiss, Manager, Research Department, The Barrett Company, New York.

SEPARATING MINERALS BY FLOATING

A Metallurgical Process Discovered by a Woman

Ores are heavier than water. Nevertheless, one method for separating the valuable portion of certain ores from the gangue depends upon the fact that the former can be made to float while the latter sinks. More than sixty years ago, it was observed that oil had a selective companionship for metal sulphides, but not until a woman investigator discovered additional facts was the flotation process for concentration of ores developed. The long-accepted story ran somewhat as follows:

Miss Carrie J. Everson, a school teacher in Denver, who had an assayer for a brother, one day washed some greasy sacks in which samples had been sent to him. Customary violent agitation of the water incidental to washing very dirty fabrics caused sulphide particles of ore coated with grease from the bags, to float as a scum. Following up this occurrence, Miss Everson discovered: that acid, added in small quantity to the pulp (pulverized ore), greatly increased the selective action of the oil; that the oiled mineral could be separated from the gangue by thorough agitation of the mass and by allowing the sulphides to float as a scum, while the gangue escaped at the bottom of the vessel. Other inventors improved the process and about the end of the 19th century rapid advance began which caught the attention of mine operators.

But the foregoing story is not correct. However, facts unearthed by the Colorado Scientific Society are quite as romantic.* Carrie Jane Billings, born at Sharon, Mass., August 27, 1842, married on November 3, 1864, William Knight Everson, a physician practicing in Chicago. He prospered and became interested in mining ventures. About 1878, he put $40,000 into the Golden Age Mining Company, of which the once illustrious Brick Pomeroy was promoter. It proved a bad investment. In an endeavor to save something from this financial catastrophe, Mrs. Everson took up the study of mineralogy. She had previously been interested in science along with her husband and had become proficient in chemistry. In 1879–80 the Doctor spent some time in Mexico for his health. During his absence, Mrs. Everson discovered the "chemical affinity of oils and fatty substances for mineral particles." On his return, Dr. Everson assisted in the research. August 4, 1886, a patent was issued to Mrs. Everson for a separation process based on their experiments. On account of the Doctor's failing health, the family removed to Denver, where he died January 20, 1889.

Unable to commercialize her patent, Mrs. Everson became a professional nurse in order to support herself and young son. She continued her investigations, nevertheless, and was joined by Charles B. Hebron, a chemist from New York, who went to Denver about 1891. He interested a Mr. Pischel, of Denver, who helped finance further experiments. March 22, 1892, a patent was issued to Mrs. Everson and Hebron, but when success seemed assured, Hebron and Pischel quarreled and the project was abandoned.

* See *Chemical and Metallurgical Engineering*, January 15, 1916, for report of the committee, George E. Collins, Philip Argall and Howard C. Parmelee.

Mrs. Everson, in the course of efforts to have her invention put to use, met Thomas F. Criley.   He and John L. Everson, her son, developed the process on a larger scale in an old stamp mill at Silver Cliff, Colorado.   Developmental work was done also in Baker City, Oregon, and at other places.   But all attempts to get financial rewards for her long and technically successful research proved unavailing.

Concluding that the industry was not ready for her process, she packed away her papers, and in 1909 removed with her son to California.   Here she lived, forgotten by mining and metallurgical men, while law suits involving millions of dollars were fought through the courts by later claimants to the flotation process.   How important her testimony might have been!   But she was not traced until 1915.   Meanwhile fire had destroyed her cottage and with it her papers, in December, 1910; her patents had lapsed, and she had died November 3, 1914, at San Anselmo and was buried in Mt. Tamalpais cemetery.   What a pity that Mrs. Everson was not found sooner and that her papers had not been kept in a safe deposit vault or other fireproof repository!

Flotation became of great importance in treating sulphide ores of copper, zinc and other metals.   Plants costing millions of dollars have been built in the United States and other countries.   Metals of great value have been recovered with profit from waste piles left by processes which made less complete recovery.   The Everson invention failed of commercial success not because it did not contain all essential principles of flotation, but because it was in advance of the metallurgical needs as then realized.

AMERICAN OPTICAL GLASS

SCIENCE SUPERIOR TO TRADITION AND TRADE SECRETS

Prior to the World War, the U. S. A. had produced only negligible quantities of optical glass. Generations of research to produce glass that would satisfy the exacting requirements had culminated in the work of two German scientists, through whose successes supremacy in the industry went to the Prussian city of Jena. Methods of manufacture were protected by secrecy. From this source came most of the high-grade optical glass used in America until very recent years. When German commerce was barred from the seas, and England and France needed all the glass they could produce, America had no alternative but to make her own. At various times subsequent to 1890, a few American glass makers had endeavored to produce optical glass; but the German glass was so excellent and cheap that there was little inducement to develop the industry until the war changed conditions and added large and urgent special demands.

Commercial manufacturers at once attacked the problem, each guarding his trade secrets. The U. S. Bureau of Standards, perceiving the exigency, began experimental work in the winter of 1914–15 at its Pittsburgh laboratory. The Geophysical Laboratory, of the Carnegie Institution of Washington, laid aside other researches and concentrated its attention upon optical glass. Later the Council of National Defense became interested through the Naval Consulting Board, and the U. S. Geological Survey assisted by finding sources of raw materials. Coöperation was established among all these parties at interest, although there was passive resistance at first in defence of trade secrets. A demonstration of the efficiency of science broke down this resistance; from analyses of 110 German glasses, a method was worked out in two or three weeks by which batches of glass could be computed so accurately in advance that with an experimental melt and one or two large melts, glass of a desired quality could be made. This was a most important advance. The method is very useful and the manner of its development indicated to the disciples of secrecy that science could be superior to technical skill, based on experience alone.

Improvements were made also in the melting pots, and in the methods of stirring the molten glass, machines being substituted for the hand labor thought indispensable at Jena In furnace operation, the cycle was shortened from two and a half days to 24 hours. In annealing, the Germans took four weeks to cool the glass very gradually from 465°C. to 370° C. America greatly reduced this period—to three days in some instances. Rolling optical glass into sheets and other innovations were successfully introduced. Percentage of usable glass in gross product reported by Germany ranged from 15 to 20; toward the end of the war, the average at one large American plant exceeded 23 per cent. The quality equaled Jena. In 1914, the U. S. A. imported practically all its optical glass; in 1918, it had become an exporter.

To comprehend the magnitude of the achievement narrated, one should understand that optical glass is not mere glass. Good optical glass must be homogeneous, both chemically and physically; must be as free as possible from color, have a high degree of transparency, extreme stability against weather and chemicals, and large measure of tough-

ness and hardness, in addition to definite refr
erties. For success, there must be had right ra
good pots, special pots for special batches, temp
trol, correct stirring. Thorough knowledge
chemistry and engineering were found to be
equivalent substitutes for experience in optical gl
German tradition to the contrary notwithstandin

Based largely upon information gathered by Harrison
"The New World of Science," edited by Robert M.
Century Co., 1920.

among all these parties at interest, although there was passive resistance at first in defence of trade secrets. A demonstration of the efficiency of science broke down this resistance; from analyses of 110 German glasses, a method was worked out in two or three weeks by which batches of glass could be computed so accurately in advance that with an experimental melt and one or two large melts, glass of a desired quality could be made. This was a most important advance. The method is very useful and the manner of its development indicated to the disciples of secrecy that science could be superior to technical skill, based on experience alone.

Improvements were made also in the melting pots, and in the methods of stirring the molten glass, machines being substituted for the hand labor thought indispensable at Jena. In furnace operation, the cycle was shortened from two and a half days to 24 hours. In annealing, the Germans took four weeks to cool the glass very gradually from 465°C. to 370° C. America greatly reduced this period—to three days in some instances. Rolling optical glass into sheets and other innovations were successfully introduced. Percentage of usable glass in gross product reported by Germany ranged from 15 to 20; toward the end of the war, the average at one large American plant exceeded 23 per cent. The quality equaled Jena. In 1914, the U. S. A. imported practically all its optical glass; in 1918, it had become an exporter.

To comprehend the magnitude of the achievement narrated, one should understand that optical glass is not mere glass. Good optical glass must be homogeneous, both chemically and physically; must be as free as possible from color, have a high degree of transparency, extreme stability against weather and chemicals, and large measure of toughness and hardness, in addition to definite refractive properties. For success, there must be had right raw materials, good pots, special pots for special batches, temperature control, correct stirring. Thorough knowledge of physics, chemistry and engineering were found to be more than equivalent substitutes for experience in optical glass making, German tradition to the contrary notwithstanding.

Based largely upon information gathered by Harrison E. Howe for "The New World ot Science," edited by Robert M. Yerkes.—The Century Co., 1920.

AMERICAN GLASS FOR SAFETY

ACHIEVEMENTS OF THE COLLABORATION OF SCIENCE WITH INDUSTRY

Time was when each railroad had its own signal colors,— greens ranging from blue-green to yellow-chrome-green, yellows from reddish yellow to green-yellow not far removed from some of the yellow greens. About 1900 there were 32 different shades of green used in American railway systems. At least one glass manufacturer carried a dozen or more sizes and styles of lens in each of these 32 shades. The situation was similar for other colors. To correct this dangerous confusion, the glass-making chemist called to his assistance the physicist and the physiological psychologist. After years of collaboration, there resulted for each color a universally adopted hue which affords maximum light transmission and maximum distinctiveness. The standard green, for instance, gives more light than other greens, and is less likely to be mistaken for yellow or blue.

An American glass-maker discovered that selenium could be made to produce a clear red of almost any depth, with the great advantage for railway signals that it transmits practically all the red rays, and, except some yellow, nothing else. Other red glasses transmit other parts of the spectrum in addition to red. Selenium ruby is used universally by American railways for danger signals, and tons of the comparatively rare element are thus consumed annually.

With the standardization of the green and red in hues which would not be mistaken for yellow it was possible to develop a yellow signal. The introduction of yellow eliminates white or clear as a fixed signal. A white light means broken glass and indicates STOP. By re-designing the semaphore lens and employing the high transmission colors, the intensity of the color signal has been greatly increased.

American glass-makers also introduced the low-expansion heat-resisting glass for railway lantern globes. A trainman's lantern is not unlikely to rest tilted on a brake ratchet or broom handle with the flame playing directly against the glass. Suddenly the lantern is carried out into the rain or snow, the overheated glass breaks, and the signal fails, jeopardizing life. For thin-walled chimneys a glass of low expansion had been successfully used abroad. It did not, however, meet satisfactorily the severe conditions to which the thick-walled railroad lantern globe was subjected. A glass was developed in this country lower in expansion than any previously made in commercial quantities. The low expansion globes, both colorless and colored, are safe and are practically the only ones now in use.

There has been a demand for a glass, which while absorbing as little of the visible spectrum as possible, would protect the eye from the short-wave-length ultraviolet. America has produced such a glass of a very pale but brilliant yellow, which almost completely absorbs the ultraviolet but transmits the visible light.

Another American glass transmits ultraviolet and absorbs the visible light. This ultraviolet has been called the invisible purple. If all other light be excluded from the room, the radiation from a mercury arc lamp transmitted by this glass, causes in the eye a puzzling and weird sensation of haze, owing to the fact that the eye cannot bring the rays to a focus as it can those of the visible spectrum. The weirdness is heightened by the ghastly appearance of eye-balls and finger nails, which like other fluorescent sub-stances, such as uranium glass, anthracene, rhodonite and willemite, change the ultraviolet to visible light, which they radiate.

For protection of operatives in electric arc welding from the radiation, which if not guarded causes serious burns of the skin and injury to the eyes, welders' glasses have been developed which absorb not only ultraviolet but also infra-red and such excess of the visible light as causes glare. The light transmitted by these glasses is in the yellow-green of the spectrum, in which visual acuity is highest.

A special pale green glass absorbs only the infra-red and transmits most of the visible light and in thickness of only 2 millimeters absorbs 95 per cent, or more, of the invisible heat rays. A piece of carbon paper so held in the rays from a projection lantern as to take fire almost at once is pro-tected indefinitely if this glass be interposed. Spectacles of this heat absorbing glass have a surprisingly comfortable and cooling effect in high temperature work.

Information on which this Narrative is based was supplied by Mr. Eugene C. Sullivan. Vice-President, Corning Glass Works.

GLASSWARE AND WARFARE

During the war, various new glasses were developed to meet exigencies. One was a glass for X-ray shields, which had about one-third the protective power of metallic lead of the same thickness. It formed part of a portable X-ray outfit used effectively at the front lines. Colored glasses for marksmen, for naval-gunners and for aviators, sextant glasses and special Fresnel ship lights were other developments for warfare.

As long ago as 1902, high grade chemical glassware was made in this country, but it took the urgency of war to bring it to a par with the best foreign ware. To-day, according to tests of the Bureau of Standards, better chemical glassware is made in this country than was ever imported, as to resistance to chemical attack, in power to withstand sudden cooling, and in mechanical strength. Army medical authorities found American flasks for preparing typhoid toxine far ahead of any flasks ever obtained abroad.

All organisms for the typhoid vaccine are grown in Kolle flasks. These flasks must be made of a glass that resists heat and mechanical shocks, is low in alkali, and the flasks must be flat so that they can be stacked. Until the European war began, all of these flasks were made in Germany. When the war cut off the supply from Germany, an American glass company had to make them. The American-made Pyrex glass is low in alkali, and resists heat and mechanical shocks better than did Jena glass; the flasks being made in iron molds, are uniform in shape, are flat, and stack well.

When Army medical men began using the lipovaccines, it was necessary to have narrow-mouthed jars for grinding the bacteria in a ball mill. All large jars were made of porcelain, but a narrow-mouthed porcelain jar had not been made in this country. Pyrex glass appeared ideal for this purpose, as jars made of it would stand heat sterilization and mechanical shocks, and the glass would not be ground off by the constant pounding of the steel balls. Pyrex glass grinding jars were made that would fit the standard ball mill frames made in this country by Abbé. In this way it became possible to prepare the lipovaccines on a large scale.

The glass baking dish is a purely American device made of a glass possessing the qualities necessary for high-grade chemical ware. Unexpectedly, baking takes place more rapidly than in metal, due to the fact that glass reflects but a few per cent of the oven heat which is radiated upon it, while a metal utensil reflects 90 per cent, or more.

During the war, the glass chemist had his glass melting pots to look after as well as his glass. German clay had been considered essential. When it could no longer be obtained, American clay batches which had previously been worked out were used. These American clay pots are giving fully as satisfactory service.

Potash glass was considered essential for incandescent electric bulbs, of which hundreds of millions are used annually. Glass chemists had developed non-potash glasses, but the uncertainties involved in the change were thought to outweigh the advantages until the war by excluding foreign potash made action imperative. Non-potash glasses, after several years, are giving better results in some respects, and except for certain special purposes a return to potash glass for bulbs is doubtful. This non-potash bulb glass, however, like the potash glass, contained 20 per cent or more, of lead. Even at its pre-war price, lead was an expensive glass-making material. Another drawback is the tradition among glass workers, that lead glass must be melted in pots. Pot melting is the old, inefficient method, supplanted by the modern tank adapted to the use of automatic conveying machinery for materials, and to machine methods of working the glass. In 1916, a tank-melted bulb glass was successfully introduced which contained neither potash nor lead, and its use has extended until a large proportion of lamp bulbs are now made of comparatively inexpensive materials, by efficient labor-saving methods adapted to large-scale production.

America's success in producing optical glass is so widely known that it needs only to be mentioned here. Its story was told in Narrative No. 22. America had achieved results in glass chemistry before the war, but the stimulus of necessity arising from the shutting off of foreign supplies, brought about more than ordinary progress. This country is now fully abreast of others, and in some respects has gone ahead, producing ware of better quality, at no increase of price to the consumer.

Information on which this Narrative is based was supplied by Mr. Eugene C. Sullivan, Vice-President, Corning Glass Works.

MEASUREMENT OF ILLUMINATION

A Defense for Human Eyes

There are bright lights in your factory, office, store. Probably you pay a large monthly bill for them. But are the machines, the typist's desks, the goods on the counter, well illuminated? A little box will tell you. It is called a "foot-candle meter."

Measurement of the candlepower of artificial light sources has occupied the attention of scientists and engineers for many years; methods and apparatus are well known. Only recently, however, has there been popular recognition of the fact that illumination is the quantity of real importance and that it, as well as candlepower, can be measured by practical engineering methods. Years ago Preece and Trotter in England produced an instrument. Scientists in Germany also produced a number of instruments, the best known of which is the Weber photometer, but in this country its use was practically confined to a few laboratories. More recently, in England, photometers for this purpose took the form of small, convenient apparatus, using a miniature incandescent lamp as a standard of reference, but capable of nothing more than relatively low precision. In Germany, quite generally, illumination photometers used flame sources for reference, but the photometric arrangements were such as to give a higher sensibility.

The first practical illumination photometer, brought out by Sharp and Millar, of New York, in 1907, used an incandescent electric lamp as a comparison lamp and a Lummer-

Brodhun cube as a photometric device. It was precise and sensitive, and moderately convenient to carry about. A small and lighter instrument was subsequently brought out by Macbath. These photometers were universal in their application, being capable of measuring illumination, candle-power and the brightness of surfaces. However, they, and all previous illumination photometers, operated on the theory that a white diffusing surface, either reflecting or transmitting, was available and could be used, which scattered all the light incident upon it in conformity with Lambert's cosine law; that is, that the brightness of the surface fell off as the direction of the incident rays varied from the normal to a grazing incidence exactly in proportion to the cosine of the angle of incidence. No surface is known for which this is true. All diffusing surfaces fail to effect perfect diffusion of the light which falls upon them at high angles of incidence, and therefore if the illumination is measured on this assumption, the measured value will in general be lower than the true value.

This difficulty was overcome by the construction in 1915 by Sharp and Little of the "compensating test-plate." In this device the diffusing surface looked at is illuminated not only from its front by the direct illumination, but also from the back in such a way that the added light from the back quite exactly compensates for the deficiency of brightness due to the lack of diffusion. It is now possible to measure illumination with all the precision required.

A more recent instrument, much simpler and more convenient, but far less accurate, is a little box, long as compared with its cross-section, with an incandescent lamp at one end and its top covered with a sheet of glass on which is fastened the equivalent of a series of little Bunsen photometric discs, stretching from one end of the box to the other. The under sides of these discs are illuminated by the lamp; this illumination falls off very rapidly with the distance from the lamp. The upper sides of the discs are subjected to the illumination to be measured. One end of the row of discs is illuminated more brightly on the outside, whereas the other end is illuminated more brightly on the inside. Therefore one end of the row appears as positives and the other as negatives. By inspection the disc can be found where the illumination on the inside is equal to that on the outside; that disc is apparently uniformly illuminated, and the illumination value is read from a scale alongside the discs.

This "foot-candle meter" has come into extensive use. It enables an unscientific observer to gain an approximate knowledge of the value of an illumination by simple inspection. It has popularized illumination measurements and has directed attention toward the importance of correct illumination. Advantages are obvious, particularly in the lighting of factories, workshops and schools, where good illumination is essential for industrial production and for defense against misuse of that most wonderful of all instruments, the human eye.

Information on which this Narrative is based was supplied by Clayton H. Sharp, Ph.D., Technical Director, Electrical Testing Laboratories, New York.

OUTWITTING THE MARINE BORERS

Port charges on ships and on goods landed could be reduced one-third if the expense caused by the destructive marine borers could be eliminated, is the estimate of a responsible harbor-engineer of a prominent port of the United States. A large element in the cost of sea-borne freights is the protection of wooden structures in salt and brackish waters against attacks of marine borers.

These borers attack commercial timbers in all seas, and are especially active in tropical waters. They destroy the sheathing of wooden ships and scows, pipe lines and tanks for salt water, spars and buoys, rafted timber, wooden piling and submerged wooden structures from mid-tide level to the mud line. They shorten the lives even of structures protected by impregnation with the creosotes used to-day. Borers lie in wait to attack treated timbers maltreated in erection, damaged by marine hazard, or incompletely infiltrated with preservative. Resin-filled knots, checks, dogholes, or crevices are sure to afford avenues of entrance for some inquisitive borer searching for a home, and others follow in his wake. Untreated piles in heavily infested waters may last but a season, while planking, pipe lines and tanks may be riddled in six weeks. The most destructive borers, *Teredo navalis* and *Limnoria lignorum*, will work near the mouths of sewers where there is tidal change, and in the presence of many industrial wastes.

There are many kinds of borers adapted to different environmental conditions, attacking wood in different ways. Some are highly modified mollusks related to the clam, but worm-like in appearance, from a few inches to four feet in length. These are the ship worms and pile worms, species of *Teredo* and *Xylotria*, which enter wood through minute holes which they excavate as larvae on the surface. As they grow they enlarge their burrows, using their growing shells as boring bits, until the wood is completely riddled, though no external evidence of the damage is visible until the pier collapses. Some molluscan borers retain their clam-like appearance. One of these, *Martesia*, attacks creosoted timbers with impunity and others (*Pholas*) bore into certain rocks.

Molluscan borers spread as eggs or as larvae, float for several weeks with currents or tides, and might be carried in ballast water or tanks of vessels for long distances. Eventually they settle down and burrow for shelter into wood. They breed generally in mid and late summer in enormous numbers and some of them spread widely from infected centers. Several hundred larvae may settle on a single square inch of exposed wood.

The most notorious of these borers is *Teredo navalis*, the pile worm of European waters, which in historic times has periodically devastated European coasts. It thrives in brackish waters and survives periodic exposures to low salinities or even to fresh water; hence in dry seasons it invades estuaries and harbors as salinities rise. Such an invasion occurred in San Francisco Bay in recent years, causing extensive destruction of untreated piling. The loss was estimated at $15,000,000. A revival of attacks in

Dutch and Scandinavian waters suggests a pandemic of this marine pest.

Adequate protection of marine structures calls for a program of correlated investigations of the chemical, engineering, and biological phases of the complicated problems centering about wood and concrete in sea water and means for protection by creosote and other preservatives. To this end the National Research Council has appointed a committee of engineers, chemists and biologists to collaborate in a carefully directed study of these problems of far-reaching significance in the cost of commerce. Who will help to advance the attack?

Contributed by Prof. C. A. Kofoid, University of California, member of the San Francisco Bay Marine Piling Committee of the American Wood-Preservers' Association.

Note, March, 1924: The Committee on Marine Piling Investigations has just completed an important part of the program which it planned. A valuable illustrated report of about 500 pages is being printed by the National Research Council.

TIGHT FLEXIBLE JOINTS FOR SUBMARINE PIPES

A Water Supply Problem

Nature made Staten Island a part of New Jersey, but Man attached it to New York City. Consequently, when demands for water from the public supply exceeded resources on the Island, Catskill Mountain water brought 120 miles had to be gotten from the nearest part of the "Greater City"; but The Narrows, two miles wide, the deep entrance to the harbor, lies between, with fast-flowing tides and heavy commerce. Many kinds of pipe and methods for laying them were considered. A heavy 36-inch cast-iron pipe with ball-and-socket joints was selected. Conditions "too numerous to mention," precluded effective employment of divers.

The problem narrowed itself to making a pipe which, beginning at Brooklyn, could be put together, link by link, like a chain, and "paid out" from a barge into the water to sink to the bottom of the dredged trench as the barge was moved, a few feet at a time, across The Narrows. The joints must be strong, but quickly made. They must be water-tight when made and so remain in spite of the bending and pulling to which they would be subjected as the pipe line was "paid out" and settled to its bearing in the trench.

The inside of each socket was turned and polished accurately to a spherical surface. A narrow band on the opposite end, or spigot, of each pipe was turned to a spherical surface to fit the inside of the socket. So far only careful foundry and machine work was required. How should the joint space between the spigot and socket be filled?

Molten lead is the common material for water pipe joints; but lead shrinks appreciably as it cools. Ordinarily this is remedied by calking, i.e., making the lead flow slightly after it is cold by blows from a hammer on a steel calking tool, thus filling the space tightly. Calking, even with powerful pneumatic hammers, failed to cause the lead to flow far enough back in the flexible joint to keep it tight after bending but a little. "Lead wool," calked in, a strand at a time, was tried; very tight joints could be made, but they would not bend readily enough and besides consumed too much time. Several alloys of lead, which like type metal would swell slightly on cooling, were tried, but none proved suitable. Other schemes were tried.

One day, while experiments on full-sized pipes were in progress in a shop near Philadelphia, the engineer in New York had a long-distance call: would he permit sixteen $\frac{1}{2}$-inch holes to be drilled through the socket of the pipe in a ring around it? A foreman had suggested that such holes be drilled and threaded so that slugs of cold lead could be forced in with strong steel screws until the shrinkage space was filled. His father, as superintendent in a refrigerating plant, made leaky joints in ammonia pipes tight by drilling small holes in the couplings and forcing bird shot in by means of "set screws." Permission was given at once. A trial showed that the method had merit. By long and careful experimentation details were perfected.

Two rows each of sixteen holes $\frac{3}{4}$ inch in diameter, were drilled around the socket of each pipe. After approximately 250 pounds of lead had been cast into each joint on the barge, 144 lead slugs $1\frac{3}{4}$ inches long and $\frac{9}{16}$ inch in diameter (total weight 26 pounds), were forced into the shrinkage space by means of steel screws operated by a special tool, and with them flake graphite and grease, as a lubricant. At first each joint was tested as made with water under 100 pounds pressure, but these joints were so uniformly tight that tests were discontinued. After the pipe line had been completed, which required two seasons with a winter's interruption, a 40-day test under 110 pounds pressure showed a leakage of only three quarts per minute from more than eight hundred joints. This is only saying in more words, that the pipe line was absolutely tight. Submarine pipes have commonly been very leaky.

By Alfred D. Flinn, formerly Deputy Chief Engineer, Catskill Aqueduct, for City of New York.

In 1924, the City is laying a second pipe line across The Narrows, of the same design, but 42 inches inside diameter.

A SERBIAN HERDSMAN'S CONTRIBUTION TO TELEPHONY

AN EXAMPLE OF THE INBORN SPIRIT OF RESEARCH

Conspicuous among hundreds of inventions which have brought America's telephone systems to their high development are those of Dr. Michael Idvorsky Pupin. They are highly scientific in character and based upon the wave transmission of sound and electricty. When the Edison Medal was presented to him in February, 1921, by the American Institute of Electrical Engineers, he told how he first became interested in sound transmission.

Although for many years an American citizen by adoption, Michael Pupin was born in a village near Belgrade, Serbia. At the age of twelve he began summer vacation service with other boys as assistant to the guardians of the villagers' herd of oxen, and at the same time his studying in Nature's own laboratory of the wave transmission of sound. Daytime duties were light; the hot sun and the hungry flies kept the wise ox in the shade. At night the cattle grazed. Moonless Serbian nights are so dark that the sky seems black even when the stars are blazing. Objects fifteen or twenty feet away cannot be seen. Only a few miles distant was the Rumanian border, and between lay extensive corn fields. When the wind blew from the corn fields to the grazing grounds, the pleasant fragance tempted the cattle; but in the corn lurked many cattle thieves. The oxen must be kept out of the corn; on the dark nights, however, they could be followed only by sound.

Now, among the arts of the herdsmen in which the boys were trained, was the art of listening through the ground. A knife with a long wooden handle was stuck in the ground. One boy who was being trained would put his ear to the handle and listen, while another boy, thirty or forty yards away, would strike his knife similarly stuck in the ground. The first boy would have to tell the direction and guess the distance. This first lesson in wave transmission set young Pupin thinking. He soon observed, as herdsmen before him had, that sounds from the knife carry much farther through hard solid ground than through plowed ground

The long nights of watching afforded much time for observing sounds and thinking about them. In the darkness the world seemed to have disappeared and the only signs of its existence were the messages of the low sounds from the grazing herd, the distant village clock, the rustling corn. Thoughts started in the lad's mind on those Serbian plains continued to evolve as he went from the village school to the academy at Prague; when he ran away from the unbearable confinement of the academy, after the freedom of the plains, and came to America, and as he made his way through many difficulties to a higher education in the sciences in the universities and laboratories of America and Europe.

Finally those germs of thought bore fruit in many scientific discoveries and inventions having to do with wave transmission, especially of sound and electricity. Among these inventions was the Pupin "loading coil," which greatly advanced the possibilities of successful long-distance telephony. A few years ago, when Chief Engineer Carty, of the Bell Telephone System, stretched his wires from the Atlantic seaboard to the Pacific coast of the United States, and President Theodore N. Vail, of "A. T. and T.," first made a human voice heard across a continent, there were Pupin coils at intervals of eight miles in that transcontinental line. In the whole world to-day there are more than three-quarter of a million Pupin coils in use in telephone lines, of which 600,000 are in the United States.

Based on information supplied by Dr. M. I. Pupin, Professor of Electro-Mechanics, Columbia University, New York.

AN EARLY ROTARY ELECTRICAL CONVERTER

THE SOLUTION OF A WELDING PROBLEM

Hermann Lemp, who has been a prolific inventor in the electrical field narrates that he first heard the name of Edison in his native Switzerland, while experimenting with a phonograph in a factory at Neuchatel. At the first International Electrical Exhibition in Paris, in 1881, he saw Edison's first steam-driven dynamo and its hundreds of incandescent lamps. Although but nineteen years of age, he decided to go to the country where such wonderful progress was being made. Before the end of the year, he was at Menlo Park, on Edison's staff.

In 1887, Lemp joined the technical staff of the Thomson-Houston Electric Company. Professor Elihu Thomson and E. W. Rice asked him to devote all his time to the commercial development of electrical welding, which he did for seven years. The welding of electric street railway rails together in place led to the construction of a large rotary converter, probably the first one of magnitude. Now such machines for changing alternating electrical current to direct current, or vice versa, are common equipment in power stations and manufacturing plants. While working on the problem of providing alternating currents from a direct-current trolley wire, the "happy thought" which took form in a rotary converter, came to him like a flash.

(But, "gentle reader," remember that back of every lightning flash is a charged cloud, and consider that back of apparently sudden discoveries and inventions, there must have been a stored mind. Ex vacuo nihil. Thorough preparation in the sciences is more than ever before necessary to useful research and successful invention.—Ed.)

Lemp's first plan for solving this problem was to couple a 500-volt direct-current motor to an alternating-current dynamo of 150 kilowatts capacity. While considering the size of the necessary apparatus, he came upon an article describing a novel electrical generator by Shuckert & Company, of Germany, which, engine-driven, had besides the usual commutator supplying direct current, slip rings from which alternating currents were collected. It occurred to Lemp that the engine was unnecessary, that the direct-current generator might be operated as a motor and that the alternating current could be taken from the slip rings. Since the company's welding transformers had been standardized on 50 cycles frequency and 350 volts, when the rotary converter was connected to a standard 500-volt trolley line, the alternating side gave 350 volts, suitable for the standard welders.

To try out the principle, a Thomson-Houston bipolar, direct-current motor of 500 volts was taken from stock; its armature was replaced by one of 250 volts, to increase speed and frequency; one of the commutator segments was grounded to the shaft, and the opposite segment was connected to a slip ring shrunk over a strip of mica laid on the commutator. The whole took about a day's time, and a standard welder when connected to this rotary converter operated perfectly.

This was an unusual engineering experience, to have two existing standard electrical systems coördinated by an intermediary without requiring all sorts of adapters, special transformers, and other apparatus.

The first welding train, built by the Johnson Company, of Johnstown, Pa., contained a 150-kilowatt rotary converter. Recently, Mr. Lemp learned that this original rail-welding equipment was still working in the streets of Lynn, Massachusetts, after having made 250,000 welds.

It is not pretended that this Narrative records the genesis of the rotary converter. It simply relates how one engineer, without previous knowledge of the work of others, solved his problem in rail welding by making a machine of the rotary converter type.

Based on information supplied by Hermann Lemp, Engineer, Erie Works, General Electric Company.

WHAT MATTER IS MADE OF

A MODERN CONCEPTION

A new picture of stuff is being painted. Fortunately for simplicity, instead of seventy or eighty, as with the atoms, we have but two new units—the positive and the negative electron. The myriads of complications which correspond to all the differences in matter about us, must reside in the arrangements or combinations of these two simple components.

Such names as electrons and atomic structure do not convey to the mind inherent relationship with radio, radium and X-rays; but a proper view of matter as it is now understood can most readily be pictured by getting the connection among some such group of present-day subjects. We are now forced to look at all matter as composed of identical, small, electrical charges, which determine the nature of chemical elements and compounds by their numbers and arrangements. An atom—the ultimate particle of a particular substance—becomes more like a solar system than like a solid. The volume of the atomic space is mainly unoccupied, but through it the forces act which are attributable to electric charges within.

Becquerel,* who found that a certain uranium ore emitted an invisible ray capable of passing through black paper and still affecting a photographic plate, was partly responsible for our new views. Soon afterward the Curies dis-

* See Narrative Number 13.

covered radium, and this was shown later to be a naturally decomposing atom. Several other decaying elements were also found. During decomposition small electrical quantities were continually discharged.

Similar discharges had already been observed in other fields, but were not understood. For example, when the filament of a lamp is heated in a high vacuum, negative electrical charges are emitted and current thus crosses the empty space. This had early been noticed by Edison. It was not until after the discovery of radium that the true nature of these "electrons" was perceived.

When these little units of negative electricity flow within a wire, they constitute the electric current. When, by high temperature, they are emitted from a metal, they are called thermions. When they pass through a gas with sufficient velocity, their impacts decompose molecules, and the greatly augmented flow of the resulting charged particles produce the common electric arc. When they flow through a vacuous space, under the influence of a high electric force, they are called cathode rays. When their motion is stopped by impact in the surface of a solid, the sudden change of motion starts an electro-magnetic wave,—an X-ray (just as a drum beat sets up a sound wave in air), and when they surge up and down wireless antennae, they produce the long wireless waves through space.

When constituent electrons are arranged in the groups called atoms, all properties seem determined merely by geography, or orientation. Apparently such old established things as chemical activity and valence are due to the number of electrons which occupy the outer surfaces of the groups. The shooting electrons of the cathode ray, stopped by the platinum or tungsten target, produce the X-rays, which by reflection in crystallized matter, disclose its atomic arrangement and thus lead to better understanding of many physical properties.

Since decomposing elements emit electrons, since heat drives them from filaments, since gases and air yield them on impact in arcs, since statically charged bodies carry them and lose them (as a car gains or loses passengers), it is logical that all electric currents are attributed to their motion, all static charges to differences in concentration, and all matter to balanced combinations of them.

Contributed by Dr. W. R. Whitney, Director, Research Laboratory, General Electric Company.

TEREDOS AND TUNNELS

ONE OF NATURE'S ENGINEERING SUGGESTIONS

Among the little marine animals which destroy wooden piles and other underwater parts of waterfront structures, probably the best known are the several varieties of shipworms, so-called, although they are not worms but molluscs. Commonly they are all comprehended in the name Teredo, in spite of the efforts of biologists for correct discrimination. Teredos bore long tunnels in wood, using their two tiny shells as excavating tools and shields for their heads. As the head advances, the body grows, excreting a calcareous lining for the tunnel. The "tail" maintains connection with the surface of the pile and can close the entrance when danger is sensed. From head to tail there is a passage through the body for the discharge of the borings into the open water. So much for Nature's prototype!

The story of the invention of the tunneling shield by which tunnel work in underwater or water-bearing ground, has been greatly simplified and its scope correspondingly enlarged is an interesting chapter in the history of modern engineering. Marc Isambard Brunel was born in France, April 25, 1769. His father, a farmer, intended him to become a priest. A strong leaning toward mathematics turned the boy in another direction and he served in the French Navy for six years. In 1792, when he returned to his native land, he found the Revolution in full swing. As he was an ardent Royalist, he came to New York and practiced land surveying and canal engineering, and also made plans for the military defences of the Narrows of New York Harbor.

In 1799, he went to England where he spent the remainder of his life. He designed and built in 1803 a complete set of wood-working machinery for the Naval Dockyard at Portsmouth. In 1812, he reorganized the system of wood-working at Woolwich and Chatham Arsenals. He was interested in steam navigation, in shoe-making machinery, in mechanical knitting. In 1818, he took out a patent (No. 4204) entitled "Method of forming tunnels or drifts under ground."* In his specifications and drawings he describes what is in essence the modern tunnel shield, to form a protection for the workers, thrust ahead by the pressure of hydraulic rams upon the finished lining. "The body, or shell, of the tunnel may be made of brick or masonry, but I prefer to make it of cast iron,"—thus foreshadowing the many miles of cast iron lining which have been built since his day.

This masterly engineer was not above going to a lowly "worm" for help and advice. His shield embodied a form of mechanical excavator. "The combination of mechanical expedients by means of which I performed the same, I denominate a Teredo, or auger, from its great analogy to that instrument, and also the vermes, known under the name of Teredo Navalis. This insect is capable of perforating the toughest timber by the power and organization of its auger-like head worked by the motion of the body enclosed within its tubular cell, which cell may be supposed to represent a tunnel."

* Quotations are from original patent application.

When it is considered that the body of the Teredo makes a closed dry chamber at the working face and that it deposits a continuous calcareous lining as it extends its tunnel, the analogy is remarkable.

Like many another genius, Brunel's financial acumen was not great, and in 1821 he was imprisoned for debt. His friends released him by payment of £5000. The latter part of his life was devoted more to civil engineering projects than to those of mechanical engineering and his great and crowning work was the construction of the Thames tunnel crossing that river between Wapping and Rotherhithe. He used a shield for this work, but one of an entirely different type from that described in his patent of 1818. The work was on a huge scale for that time with the appliances and methods then at hand. This tunnel was rectangular in section, 23 feet high by 37 feet wide, or equal to a circle nearly 33 feet in diameter, which is larger than any sub-aqueous tunnel since built. The river broke in several times, and the work was not finished until 1843. Helped by his son, Isambard Kingdom Brunel, he conquered each disaster as it came. The anxieties and the days and nights spent in the tunnel proved too much. He suffered a paralytic stroke in 1843, another in 1845 and died in London, December 12, 1849.

Contributed by B. H. M. Hewett, of Jacobs & Davies, Consulting Engineers for the Hudson River and other tunnels.

A FARMER'S PHENOLOGICAL RECORDS

A Tale of Remarkable Individual Research with a
A Sad Sequel of Loss Due to Isolation

Thomas Mikesell, of Wauseon, Ohio, was a western boy
with a high-school education. On return from service in
the Union army in the Civil war, he engaged in farming,
and became interested in weather phenomena, especially
their relation to the growth of plants. Beginning in 1883,
for thirty years, he kept the most complete, accurate and
extensive records of a phenological nature which have ever
been undertaken, including rainfall, temperature and other
weather conditions, carrying them on in conjunction with
his regular farm operations. This work was undertaken
purely through a scientific interest in the subject, in a
modest manner and without the slightest idea that the
results might later prove almost invaluable.

For more than 150 species of plants Mikesell kept accurate
records, with scarcely a single observation missing in thirty
years, of every phase of plant growth from the time the
buds started until the plant was divested of leaves in the
fall. Similar records were kept of the times of migration,
dates of nesting, and other life incidents, for a large variety
of birds. A few years ago, J. Warren Smith, then local
Weather Bureau official, who had learned of the existence of
these records, obtained from Mikesell permission to copy a
considerable portion thereof. They were published by the
United States Government and have attracted wide attention. They have been used as materials for many scientific

investigations in relation to agriculture and plant economics, and formed perhaps the most important basis for the formulation of certain rules promulgated during the late war to assist farmers in determining dates of planting and seeding which would insure maximum crop yields during the war period.

Although the portion of Mikesell's phenological records published by the Government comprise many closely printed quarto pages, yet they represent but a small fraction of the complete series of observations. It is said that Mrs. Mikesell strongly opposed her husband in the conduct of these researches, deeming them a waste of time. Shortly after Mikesell's death, an effort was made to recover the remaining records for publication, only to learn that they had been destroyed! An irreparable loss.

Mikesell attempted but few deductions from his data, yet his work was a scientific research of the highest order in that no essential detail likely to be needed for future deductions from the data appears to have been omitted. It is at once apparent how much may be accomplished by an enthusiastic individual in scientific research, but it is even more apparent that there should be some organization standing behind the individual to encourage him and afford means for publication of the results obtained from time to time, thus making them earlier available and also avoiding the possibility of lamentable losses such as occurred in this instance.

———

This tale will recall to readers of these Research Narratives the temporary failure of Gregor Mendell (Narrative No. 1, "The Story of Mendellism") and the loss of valuable records

which befell Mrs. Everson (Narrative No. 21, "Separating
Minerals by Floating"), both of which might have been
avoided through connection with suitable organizations,
had such organizations existed or been accessible in their
times.—*Editor*.

By Robert E. Horton, Consulting Hydraulic Engineer, Voorheesville,
N. Y.

THE NAVAL TORTOISE SHELL

John Stevens, of Hoboken, New Jersey, is credited with first proposing metal armor plates for ships' sides. During the war of 1812, he offered the U. S. Government plans for a vessel with her guns protected by inclined armor. More than a generation passed before his idea was used. Although the United States probably was the first country to start construction of armored ships, France put the first vessels of this type into commission. October 17, 1855, the first ironclad squadron ever seen, the Devastation, the Love and the Tounante, silenced the Russian forts at Kinburn.

Sixty years ago, in the waters of Virginia, the Merrimac and the Monitor fought a battle which sealed the fate of wooden warships, already made obsolete. A revolving turret for naval vessels had been patented by Theodore R. Timby, of Poughkeepsie, New York, in 1842, but never used. Captain John Ericsson, by his invention, combined a turret, heavy iron armor, and 11-inch Dahlgren guns into a new fighting machine which looked like "A Yankee cheese box on a plank." It stopped the big ironclad, which had been almost equally revolutionary the day before in its destruction of some of the finest wooden warships in the American navy.

Already competition between armor plate on one hand and guns and projectiles on the other hand was keen. Developments in the metallurgy of steel and advances in mechani-

95

cal and naval engineering soon brought the beginning of the evolution of modern war vessels.

By the mid seventies, wrought iron armor had reached its limit. Rifled guns and improved projectiles had won. Then came steel armorplate. Competitive tests at Spezia, Italy, in 1876, with plates 22 inches thick conclusively demonstrated the superiority of steel, and the manufacture of wrought iron armor ceased thereafter. Compound armor, with a hard steel face welded to a wrought iron back gained favor, but was completely outclassed in a test at the Annapolis proving ground in September, 1890. Homogeneous and nickel-steel plates then had some success in competition with the guns.

About 1888 while H. A. Harvey, of Newark, New Jersey, was visiting the Washington gun factory, Captain Folger, the superintendent, suggested that he apply to armor plates his method for hardening tool steel. Harvey soon devised a surface-hardening process, to which his name became attached; it affects the steel to a depth of about one inch to one and a half inches, according to the time given to the treatment. An armor plate made by Schneider & Co., of France, Harveyised in America, was tested at Annapolis on March 14, 1891. Although cracked, it stopped and shattered the projectiles. The Secretary of the Navy immediately signed a contract for Harveyising the armor for U. S. men-of-war. Surface-hardened plates came into general use. Harveyised plates are so hard that they cannot be machined; they can only be ground. Hence, the plates had to be shaped and necessary holes drilled before hardening.

After adopting Harveyised armor plate, the U. S. Navy experienced difficulties in certain details of construction because of the impossibility of drilling holes into the hardened surface. On the sample Harveyised plates submitted the problem was thought solved by covering with clay during the carbonizing process, the local spots desired to remain soft. Such spots were painted white. Commercial plates when delivered on board ship, though painted white in spots, proved to be hard all over. Diamond drills, oxy-hydrogen flame and other means were tried unsuccessfully. Hermann Lemp, who was then in the laboratories, of the Thomson-Houston Company, at Lynn, Massachusetts, narrates that after a few trials, he learned that the problem was not so much how properly to heat a spot in the plate as how to cool it gradually below the "chilling point" by gradually removing the heating source which was done by slowly diminishing the electric current used to heat the spot to be drilled. After this treatment, spots and strips in armor plates could be drilled and tapped with ease. Commercial apparatus was promptly furnished to the Cramps' shipyard in Philadelphia and to the Union Iron Works at San Francisco, permitting the speedy finishing of the Massachusetts and the Oregon, the first Harveyised battleships. England wrestled with another problem. The oblong port holes for large guns in their conical turrets could not be cut after Harveyising and would warp out of shape if cut before Harveyising. Reluctantly soft nickel-steel armor was temporarily specified for these turrets. By moving slowly the electrical annealing apparatus along a designated line, thereby withdrawing gradually the heating source from any particular spot, a strip could be annealed permitting the cutting of the port holes after Harveyising. Thus, also, Sir William White was enabled to issue his order that all her

Majesty's ships should be Harveyised from stem to stern. These annealing sets were supplied to every country possessing a navy.

In 1921, the nation that so often led in advancing naval offensive and defensive armament gained the coöperation of the other great naval powers in calling a halt.   Incidentally, the arts of peace have gained much from naval "necessities," but the cost has been very great.

Based on information from various sources.

COMPRESSED AIR FOR UNDERWATER TUNNEL CONSTRUCTION

A Means for Making Practicable Many Difficult Foundations and Tunnels

Many a bridge pier, many a tunnel and the foundations for many a modern "skyscraper" would have been impossible but for the use of compressed air. The story of the invention of compressed air equipment is another interesting chapter in the history of modern engineering. The character who conceived the application of air under pressure to tunnels in order to keep the water from flowing into the workings, was, possibly, even more picturesque than Brunel, inventor of the tunnel shield, to whom Narrative No. 31 was devoted.

Thomas Cochrane, the son of Archibald Cochrane, Ninth Earl of Dundonald, was born in Scotland, December 14, 1775. Like Brunel, Cochrane served in the Navy; he went to sea in 1793 and remained in service until 1851, becoming an admiral. He acquired a deserved reputation for skill and daring and took a leading part in several severe and successful engagements. He was elected to Parliament and made a mark as a radical reformer of everything and everyone, excepting himself. Like Brunel, he got into the meshes of the law; it was on a charge of fraud on the Stock Exchange, in which he speculated heavily. He, his uncle, and some others were convicted, fined and imprisoned for one year. It came natural to a man of his temperament to escape from prison. He was recaptured, but regained his liberty on payment of £1000. In the intervals of fighting at sea, denouncing abuses and speculating on the Exchange, he was busy with scientific invention.

Among many inventions, mostly having to do with the propulsion of ships, he took out a memorable patent (No. 6018) on October 20, 1830, described an "Apparatus to facilitate excavating, sinking and mining."* It is not too much to say that the entire process of placing a tunnel or shaft under compressed air for the purpose of holding back the water and thus making the work easier, or possible, is here exactly foreshadowed and described. "An iron cylinder, or shaft, is first sunk vertically to the level of the intended tunnel. The shaft is fitted with an air-tight top and ante-chamber, or lock, by means of which men may enter the shaft without escape of air. Air is pumped into the shaft and kept at a continuous pressure. The men enter the lock, close the outer door and open communication with the shaft, by which the pressure in the antechamber becomes that of the shaft, upon which the shaft door may be opened for the men to enter."

"After the tunnel has been excavated for some distance, a partition and double doors may be put up to retain air more highly compressed within the tunnel, and similarly several such compartments may be made by which the strain on the various doors may be distributed."

There is but little doubt that the tremendous difficulties of Brunel with the Thames tunnels must have inspired Cochrane with the idea of the application of compressed air to such work, and it is said that Dr. Colladon, a noted physicist of that period, called Brunel's attention to Coch-

* Quotations are from original patent application.

rane's proposal. Brunel did not adopt the idea. It was not until 1879 that Cochrane's plan was put into effect, at two widely separated places, at New York by Haskins for his Hudson River tunnel, and on a much smaller scale by Hersent at Antwerp. Lord Dundonald died in London, October 30, 1860, and was buried in Westminster Abbey.

His idea was, doubtless, derived from the diving bell which had been known since the days of Alexander the Great and Julius Cæsar, and which was a source of much interest all through the Middle Ages. A bell was invented by Kleingert in 1798, by which the diver was supplied with air at a pressure corresponding to the depth of water, and Brize-Fradin in 1808, made improvements in the ventilation of diving bells, cooling the compressed air with ice and using caustic soda to absorb the exhaled carbon dioxide gas.

Without compressed air, the tunneling shield and the caisson, many of our most remarkable civil engineering works would have been impracticable. The caisson is only a vertical modification of the tunnel shield, used for excavating the foundations of bridges and buildings.

Mr. Clemens Herschel quotes Eliot C. Clarke as authority for the statement that he worked in the Detroit tunnel under air pressure about 1872 or 1873. It is recorded by still another authority that this railroad tunnel was begun in 1872 and abandoned in 1873.—*Editor*.

Contributed by B. H. M. Hewett, of Jacobs & Davies, Consulting Engineers for the Hudson River and other tunnels.

THE DISCOVERY OF MANGANESE STEEL

Its Metallurgical Paradoxes

Hadfield's discovery of manganese steel as a result of research practically started the study of alloy steels. Before him, Mushet had, indeed, worked out empirically a self-hardening steel for metal-cutting tools, but it gave no such impetus to research in the field of useful metals. As a young man Hadfield started experimenting in his father's steel foundry to see if he could find a hard steel suitable for tramcar wheels. He melted his mixtures in crucibles and tested his products by the means then at hand,—the file, chisel, forge, magnet, and hardening and tempering. These were enough to enable him when he first made an alloy coming within the definition of maganese steel to realize that he was dealing with a new metal.

Before his time, everyone who had tried the effect of increasing manganese in steel had found that the steel was made harder and less ductile with each increase, so that if 2.5 per cent were present the product was too hard and brittle to be of any use. The highest proportion ever added had been 3.5 per cent, which made the steel even more brittle. Naturally it was believed that more manganese would merely result in still greater weakness.

Hadfield, however, took nothing for granted but tried everything and as a result found the new alloy which, when it contained about 13 per cent of manganese, and was properly heat-treated, had maximum combined properties of strength and toughness. He told his father, Robert Hadfield, and his

102

superintendent, Mr. Mallaband, about his discovery. They were naturally skeptical and told him that he would better repeat his experiments. He did so with the same result and then they began to take notice.

Here was a high-carbon steel which in several ways was the opposite of what would be expected by any one familiar with iron. A magnet would not attract it, and when heated to a bright orange heat and cooled quickly, as by immersion in cold water, it was given extraordinary ductility. There were other less notable features but these were enough to excite astonishment.

Naturally, the first attempts to adapt the new hard metal were for cutting purposes, particularly for metals, but experiments in that direction came to naught. The great field for this steel, resistance to abrasion, particularly by earthy materials such as rocks and ores, was not fairly recognized until ten years after the steel was first made.

The discovery, as the result of systematic research, of a metal having such unique properties as manganese steel, started other steel-makers to see whether additional useful alloys could be found. As a result of these activities, which eventually extended throughout the civilized world, many alloy steels have been developed of exceeding importance, which have advanced materially the useful arts and particularly the conquest of distance on land, in the air and under the sea.

This discovery also argues strongly for research even without a definite object. Hadfield was searching for a hard steel for another purpose. He had no idea of finding a non-magnetic or water-toughening steel. So anyone has a chance of finding something new and useful in any systematic investigation or research which explores any unknown field of knowledge.

As usual the inventor's reward was in this case an extremely small part of the benefit of manganese steel to the world. Years passed before the various uses for the steel were found. Everyone disbelieved when told of it. Trials for the various purposes had to be made to show its fitness. The development of the business side called for the liberal expenditure of time, effort and money. The life of the patent, fourteen years, is too short a time to enable the inventor of anything of such extreme novelty to be suitably recompensed in a business way, though he may, as Sir Robert has, find satisfaction in having forwarded the welfare of the world in so great a degree.

Contributed by Henry D. Hibbard, Consulting Engineer, Plainfield, New Jersey.

A STORY OF VELOX

Numerous Americans are, or have been, photographers of one variety or another. To most of them the name Velox is familiar. Few, however, know of the years of hard work, the patient research, the repeated discouragements, the slow process of education which preceded success. As far back as 1883, L. H. Baekeland, who was an enthusiastic amateur photographer, while still a student in the University of Ghent, invented this process. He was graduated in 1884, and a few years later won the first prize in chemistry in a competition among the alumni graduated within three years from the four Belgian universities. This prize included a traveling scholarship, which brought him to the United States in 1889. Here he made acquaintanceships that led to professional engagements in the manufacture of photographic films and papers.

In 1893, with Leonard Jacobi, he established the Nepera Chemical Company in Yonkers, New York. They began on a small scale the manufacture of photographic papers. Other investigators had substituted silver-chloride for silver-bromide emulsions, but without change of process—namely, precipitation and ripening, followed by washing. By committing "photographic heresy" in omitting the washing entirely, Baekeland found he could make a silver-chloride which was relatively insensitive to yellow rays, and could be manipulated by candle or gas light, if not brought too near. As to speed, the new paper was incomparably inferior to bromide paper or ordinary chloride of silver paper. But he realized the important fact that by exposing quite close to the artificial light, and developing at a safe distance (a few feet) this apparent defect could be turned to great practical advantage.

Do not imagine that everything went smoothly. In 1893 came the famous business panic. Then there was more than the usual share of technical troubles. For instance, while excellent paper could be made in temperate weather, it became practically hopeless to do so in hot summer days. The remedy seemed easy—to rectify the temperature by artificial cooling, but this had not the desired effect. After a while special scientific investigation disclosed the fact that the troubles were due not so much to temperature as to the moisture in the air. This led to installing a refrigerating system over which the air could be drawn first, so as to extract its moisture by precipitating it as ice, after which the dried air could be sent over heated pipes so as to raise its temperature to the proper degree before it entered the paper coating machinery.

Manufacturers in Europe, where the moisture in the air does not vary to such extraordinary extent, had scarcely any conception of the difficult problems encountered in the United States, where in winter the air is so dry as to cause electric sparks, while in the summer the air is often so saturated that many objects condense humidity at temperatures as high as 76 degrees Fahrenheit. Photographs made with inferior processes may last many years if kept in Europe, but frequently deteriorate here in a few weeks in summer. A simple test distinguished which kind of prints were most likely to fade. By cutting a photograph in two and exposing

one-half in a jar to the fumes of ammonium-hydrosulphide a
few hours showed the same amount of fading as would have
been produced under ordinary conditions after months or
years.

Upon these experiments was based the manufacture of
several sensitized papers which could be unhesitatingly recom-
mended as giving permanent prints. One of these papers
was called Velox on account of the speed with which the
prints could be made independently of weather conditions.
Baekeland was firmly convinced that this process had a great
future. Unfortunately, the public did not think so at all.
In fact, it was disappointing to notice how every photographer, amateur or professional, was wedded to the older
processes and would have nothing to do with the method
about which he felt so enthusiastic. His best friends and
others did not hesitate to tell him that there was no chance
whatsoever for this new method, because "it was so much
simpler and easier to print in the sun," to which everybody
was accustomed.

Later he realized that most of these people *knew too much*
and never gave themselves the trouble of even glancing at the
printed directions; they were, like so many other persons,
past learning anything new. Finally, success came from the
most unexpected quarters. A new generation of modest
amateurs began to read and follow directions. To the dis-
gust of their more experienced friends who "knew it all,"
they showed excellent prints on the new paper, better in
several respects than experienced men had produced with
older processes. It required four years of hectic work and
strenuous introduction before the business began to show
slight profit. Two years more, and the enterprise began to

prosper rapidly. In 1899, it was sold, at a good price, to the Eastman Kodak Company, sixteen years after the beginning in Ghent.

Prepared from information supplied by Dr. Leo Hendrik Baekeland, New York.

PATTERN-SHOP RESEARCH

Early Development of Hydraulic Turbines

Poet and painter familiarized the populace with the picturesque water wheels along the streams of many countries, which but a generation or two ago, drove the machinery of small mills. For the most part, those wheels were of low efficiency. From them to the turbines of tens of thousands of horse-power which harness Niagara and many another "big drop," is a long step in water power development. Poets have not yet learned the song of these new giants, with their allies, the modern electric generator and the high tension transmission line, nor have painters yet made them picturesque. They are, none the less, full of poetry of achievement.

Early in the 19th century, French inventors produced turbines in which the water flowed in a direction generally parallel with the axis of the rotating part, or runner, and turbines in which the water flowed outward or less radially through the runner. These simpler types could be used only for relatively small capacities and slow speeds. Then came the development in America of the inward flow type, the work of no one inventor. Samuel B. Howd, of Geneva, New York, patented such a turbine in 1836, which closely resembles the most modern types in its principle. While more compact and giving a higher speed than the French turbine, it was still a wheel of small capacity. James B. Francis, of Lowell, Massachusetts, improved its mechanical construction and efficiency.

Probably the greatest achievement of any one man in advancing the development of the hydraulic turbine was that of John B. McCormick, of Indiana County, Pennsylvania. He had a little sawmill on a small stream, and could run only a pondful at a time. The wheel was too large and used water so rapidly that it drew down the pond quickly and so curtailed operations. As in many other old sawmill wheels, there was no satisfactory way of reducing the quantity of water used. Like most early turbines and those of the present day as well, the water passages through the runners or buckets, as they are called, were narrower at the outlet than at the inlet to the wheel. McCormick conceived the idea that by still further extending the buckets he would make the outlets still narrower, thus choking the discharge, reducing the quantity of water used, and conserving the pondage. To accomplish this he rivetted sheet iron extensions on to the outlets of the buckets, keeping the same form as the original passages but making them longer, narrower and more curved. To his great surprise and gratification he found not only that the quantity of water used was reduced, but that in spite of using less water, the power of the wheel was considerably increased. This led him to further experiments.

About 1870, McCormick found that by extending the bucket vanes of an inward flow turbine downward and outward, making them ladle or spoon shaped, he was able greatly to increase the outlet openings of a turbine of a given diameter. At the same time, the length or depth of the inlet openings was proportionately increased, thus greatly increasing the capacity without increasing the diameter of the runner. Since the speed of a turbine decreases as the diameter increases, he thus produced a turbine of much greater capacity without reducing the speed. It was also found that the use of curved vanes providing for downward and outward flow, as well as inward flow through the runner, increased the efficiency since the water left the wheel in a direction opposite to that of the motion of the runner and so dropped away from the runner with little absolute velocity.

Not being able to analyze his intricate problem mathematically, McCormick depended upon his aptitude for mechanics, his keen observation and a sense of the action of the water in passing through the wheel. He worked on his wooden patterns with his own hands, making them express the results of his latest observations on trials of his wheels at the testing flume in Holyoke, or their preformance in service. By trial and modification, he steadily advanced the efficiency of his turbines. His work was almost revolutionary. He laid the foundation for the great advances of recent years.

McCormick's designs were, however, arbitrary and each size or pattern was worked out by long and costly experimentation. Although the theory of the hydraulic turbine had been evolved mathematically many years before, it was never successfully applied to the design of turbines to meet specific conditions until after the advent of hydroelectric power transmission. The next step in advance consisted in the modification of the combined-flow, or McCormick, turbine largely by means of theoretical deductions so as to adapt it to speeds, capacities and other conditions different from those for which the experimental designs were made. Furthermore, the growth in the size of units made the McCormick method of pattern-shop research no longer practicable.

Based upon information supplied by Robert E. Horton, Consulting Hydraulic Engineer, Voorheesville, New York.

SMELTING TITANIFEROUS IRON ORE

PROSPECTOR AND RESEARCHER

This story begins with a prospector. Most stories dealing with mining and metallurgy can be traced back to the pioneer who seeks his fortune amid the wild hills and rocks.

In 1913, a prospecting party in Canada, searching for gold, ran across some peculiar looking iron ore. They recognized it as titaniferous ore; but that did not satisfy them. Being prospectors trained in science, they followed up their work in the field with work in the laboratory. Qualitative tests for radium, molybdenum, nickel, and cobalt gave traces at most. When it came to vanadium, a beautiful violet-blue color demonstrated the presence of that rare metal. Then the fun began.

Being impecunious, these prospectors got financial backing, went off to the woods in the Spring, and staked out four miles of claims along their iron range. They hired an accomplished analyst, who sent them telegrams that reeked with vanadium.

With ore running from two to five per cent of the precious metal, its price at six dollars a pound, and millions of tons of ore in sight, things seemed too good to be true. They were. Samples of ore were sent to half a dozen consulting chemists, and the opinion of these was unanimous—there was no vanadium to be found, or at best only traces.

The war provided a merciful hiatus.

Not content with the judgment of their analysts, the prospectors, now reduced to two in number, tackled their problem again in 1919. They remembered very clearly that

112

violet-blue color. They searched for and found a reliable method of analysis for vanadium in the presence of titanium (Cain's method); then, after a long study of the old reliable Periodic table, discovered a brand new method of smelting iron ore. They mixed titaniferous ore with sand as flux, ran it through an electric reducing furnace, and got pig-iron containing all the vanadium in the ore (a highly satisfactory quantity), and a beautifully fluid slag. This was confirmed in large-scale experiments, and then followed up by two years of research under the auspices of the Advisory Research Council of Canada. This research established the chemical control of the operation. Now steps are being taken to apply the process commercially.

Thus, there is demonstrated, once more, the usefulness of research. Without it, the world's huge deposits of titaniferous iron ore would remain unused for decades, or for centuries, or forevermore. With it, we may get vanadium alloy steel for our automobiles at half its present price. And when cost is greatly reduced, new uses for a material are commonly found.

Contributed by W. M. Goodwin, Editor, *Canadian Mining Journal*, Gardenvale, Province of Quebec.

THE BIRTH OF BAKELITE: ITS GROWTH

AN ADVENTURE WITH SYNTHETIC RESINS

Bakelite was born of formaldehyde and phenol, but it was only through very scientific matchmaking that this union was brought about. Other substances may be used, for example, cresol and hexamethylentetramin. Formaldehyde in reacting upon phenol does not necessarily give bakelite. It is only under very special conditions, now well established by the research work of Baekeland, that this substance can be obtained. In fact, when formaldehyde is let to react on phenol under ordinary conditions, almost anything may happen but the formation of bakelite.

A number of investigators worked in this field but without producing any result which gave promise of commercial success. One, for example, obtained insoluble, irregular masses which he could not control. Baekeland sought a solvent for this worthless product, hoping to make a varnish superior to all existing varnishes. After many attempts, he had to give up the quest.

Then he changed his tactics. If nothing could be done with the substance after it was once produced in a flask, he would generate the substance right on the spot where he wanted it, inside the fibers of wood. He encountered endless difficulties. Certain classes of wood instead of becoming harder, became softer. He also noticed that chemical reactions in these capillary conditions proceed in a very different way than in a flask, for the reason that the chemical dynamics in capillary spaces are considerably disturbed. The carbolic acid (phenol), before it had time to react upon the formaldehyde had every opportunity for destroying the fibre.

This led to a long systematic laboratory investigation. When he was through he had established practically all important facts on which are based the industrial processes of bakelite. Under certain conditions, he could separate the process into steps; one of the first steps was the production of a certain intermediary substance which, although it had the general appearance of a resin on account of its brittleness, its solubility and its fusibility, differed radically from the natural resins by the fact that as soon as heated at a certain temperature it changed into an entirely different body incomparably harder and stronger than the original resinous material and which, furthermore, looked like natural amber although it was much stronger and no longer melted if heated, and was insoluble in all known neutral solvents.

He discovered also the important fact that the presence of ammonia, or another base, in suitable proportions, will surely make the reaction go the right way toward the production of the infusible product, while with the presence of an acid, the formation of permanently fusible resins will be favored in case the amounts of carbolic acid are preponderant; that furthermore, the use of a suitable base in proper quantities gives an easy means of controlling the reaction at whatever phase is desirable.

The mechanical properties of these infusible condensation products were enormously improved by the introduction of fibrous substances, for example, wood fibre or asbestos. Many other facts were established by his work. He not only pointed out unmistakable methods for producing every time, at will, either a fusible or an infusible resin, but he gave the explanation why in one case one substance and in another case a different one was obtained when starting from the same raw materials.

Since he published his patents and read his papers before the American Chemical Society, there have been started here and in Europe numerous factories where these processes are used for the most varied purposes, ranging from a billiard ball to wireless, or radio, apparatus; from a self-starter for automobiles to transparent fountain pens, this range of varieties embracing switchboards for battleships, moldings for kodaks, phonograph records, casings for instruments of precision, armatures and commutators for dynamos and motors, telephone receivers, railroad signals, grinding wheels, machine gears, airplane propellers, umbrella handles, buttons, cigar holders and pipe stems, articles of ornament and many other varieties.

Prepared from information supplied by Dr. Leo Hendrik Baekeland, New York.

PALLADIUM

DANGER IN DISCREDITING THE UNLIKELY

A single serious error has, in some instances, caused an investigator to abandon science. The following example is given by Dr. Thomson:—Chenevix was for several years a most laborious and meritorious chemical experimenter. It is much to be regretted that he should have been induced, in consequence of the mistake into which he fell respecting palladium, to abandon chemistry altogether.

Palladium was originally made known to the public by an anonymous handbill which was circulated in London, announcing that palladium, or new silver, was on sale at Mrs. Forster's, and describing its properties. Chenevix, in consequence of the unusual way in which the discovery was announced, naturally considered it as an imposition upon the public. He went to Mrs. Forster's, and purchased the whole of the palladium in her possession, and set about examining it, prepossessed with the idea that it was an alloy of some two known metals. After a laborious set of experiments, he considered that he had ascertained it to be a compound of platinum and mercury, or an amalgam of platinum, made in a peculiar way which he describes. The paper was read at a meeting of the Royal Society by Dr. Wollaston, who was Secretary, and afterwards published in their "Transactions."

Soon after this publication another anonymous handbill was circulated, offering a considerable price for every grain of palladium made by Mr. Chenevix's process, or by any other process whatever. No person appearing to claim the money

117

thus offered, Dr. Wollaston, about a year after, in a paper read to the Royal Society, acknowledged himself to have been the discoverer of palladium, and related the process by which he had obtained it from the solution of crude platina in aqua regia, incident to his process of manufacturing platinum. There could be no doubt, after this, that palladium was a peculiar metal, and that Chenevix, in his experiments, had fallen into some mistake, probably by inadvertently employing a solution of palladium instead of a solution of his amalgam of platinum, and thus giving the properties of one solution to the other.

It is very much to be regretted that Dr. Wollaston allowed Chenevix's paper to be printed without informing him, in the first place, of the true history of palladium; most assuredly, if he had been aware of the bad consequences that were to follow, and that it would ultimately occasion the loss of Chenevix to the science, he would have acted in a different manner. More than once in the course of conversation on the subject, Dr. Wollaston gave assurance that he did everything that he could do, short of betraying his secret, to prevent Chenevix from publishing his paper; that he had called upon him and assured him that he himself had attempted his process without being able to succeed, and that he was satisfied that he had fallen into some mistake. As Chenevix still persisted in his conviction of the accuracy of his own experiments after repeated warnings, perhaps it is not very surprising that Dr. Wollaston allowed him to publish his paper, though, had he been aware of the consequences to their full extent, he certainly would not have done so. It comes to be a question whether, had Dr. Wollaston informed him of the whole secret, Chenevix would have been convinced.

An instructive moral may be drawn by a scientific investigator from this example, especially the great danger of being too strongly impressed with a preconceived idea, and the duty of not holding an hypothesis as if it were a fixed truth. Nothing, also, so effectually destroys the motives for research and the pleasure of such occupation, as to find, after having made and published a laborious investigation, that the conclusion was all a mistake.

History of Chemistry, vol. ii, p. 216, Thomson.—G. Gore, LL.D., F.R.S., in "The Art of Scientific Discovery."

ALCHEMISTIC SYMBOLS

The pursuit of new knowledge, one modern phase of which is scientific research, has always met opposition. So strong was this opposition by the established order in olden days that it sometimes led to social abasement, torture or death. Hence the necessity for secrecy and the use of symbols. In remote centuries, enterprising men began to experiment with the things that made up their physical surroundings. By slow stages an art grew which came to be called chemy and later alchemy. Very early in the days of alchemy, the commoner substances were represented in writings of the alchemists by symbols, and likewise many operations of their art. The origins of these symbols are sometimes easily recognized; sometimes the symbols seem to have been products of the fancy. Among the most ancient are those used for the metals; their germ is to be found in the earliest days of history.

In the misty times of the past, there lived on the great plain at the head of the Persian Gulf a race whose wisdom was famed to surpass that of all surrounding peoples. In the clear atmosphere of that region they watched from the summits of high mounds the stars and the planets, seeking to trace a connection between the heavenly bodies and the affairs of earth. Here, among the Chaldeans, was born astrology, the mother of astronomy. Here, too, are found the beginnings of alchemy, which three thousand or more years later was to develop into the science of chemistry.

The Chaldeans associated the metals known to them with the planets, and believed that through their influence the metals grew in the earth. The planets in turn were closely connected with the gods and goddesses of the pantheon of mythology. This threefold association of metals, planets and divinities seems for many centuries to have been dormant, but was revived by the alchemists, and by them the metals were always called by the name of the planet. In gold was typified the bright yellow glow of the sun, in silver,

Symbol	Name	Symbol	Name	Symbol	Name
	Air		Arsenic		Platinum (White Gold)
	Fire		Bismuth		Silver (Luna, Moon)
	Water		Copper (Venus)		Sulphur
	Antimony		Iron (Mars)		Tin (Jupiter)
	Gold (Sol. Sun)		Mercury		Nickel
	Lead (Saturn)		Zinc		Acid

the soft white light of the moon; in iron, the weapons of Mars, the war-god; in copper, Venus Anadyomene, rising, full-formed, in all her beauty from the ocean's foam on the shore of the island of Cyprus, from which comes the name of copper. Lead, which, however we may polish it, soon loses its brightness, was the metal of Saturn, dullest of all the gods. Tin, known in early times only in bronze, its alloy with copper, was the metal of Jupiter, who, under the name Bel, was always associated by the Chaldeans with Venus, called by them Beltis. Finally in quicksilver was found the fitting type of Mercury, fleet-footed messenger of the gods. Some of these designations have been retained even to the present: quicksilver is commonly known as mercury, silver nitrate is called lunar caustic, and saturnine poisoning prevails among lead-workers.

In the old alchemistic writings we find the names of the metals very generally written with the astronomical symbols of the planets, and from these symbols has been developed, through many changes, the present simple system of one-letter and two-letter abbreviations used in modern chemistry.

When platinum was discovered, it was first called L'or blanc (white gold), and hence to it was given a symbol combining those of gold and silver, platinum resembling gold in its noble qualities, being unattacked by any single acid, unoxidizable, fusible with difficulty and of high specific gravity, and resembling silver in its color. Many other and more obscure symbols were gradually introduced, until in one alchemistic manuscript of the early part of the seventeenth century no less than twenty-two symbols and thirty-three distinct names are used for mercury alone.

But, with all its ignorance, as we now consider it, and with all its deceit, it was out of this maze of alchemy, with its transmutation of metals and its philosopher's stone, that the chemistry of to-day was at length evolved.

Abridged from a brochure by James Lewis Howe, Washington and Lee University, written for Baker & Co., Inc.

TEMPERATURES OF STARS

By study of distant stars, knowledge of our own earth and Sun is being extended. Improvements in the telescope, and invention of the spectroscope about 1859 by Gustav Kirchhoff and Robert Bunsen made possible the determination of the chemical elements in our own Sun and many others. In recent years the spectroscope has been applied also to measurement of temperatures of stars, and there have been discovered temperatures as high as 10,000°C. far above any which man has hitherto succeeded in creating. The highest temperature known to have been produced on the earth is 5500°C. in the tungsten arc under high pressure, at Nela Research Laboratory, Cleveland, Ohio.

Many observations on stellar temperatures have been made by Coblentz at the Lick Observatory, Mt. Hamilton, California, in 1914, and at the Lowell Observatory, Flagstaff, Arizona, in 1921 and in 1922. In 1914, he used very sensitive vacuum thermocouples and passed the star's light through a tiny water cell. The water cell has the property of absorbing the invisible infra-red rays which are emitted by stars of low luminosity. Hence, it is a useful device for studying double stars, like Sirius, which have companions of low luminosity and for searching for double stars which may have dark companions.

The transmission screens of water, quartz and different kinds of glass, adopted in 1921, made it feasible to obtain for the first time some knowledge of the energy distribution of stars, and demonstrated what astronomers did not know before, that the photographic plate, when properly standardized will be a useful adjunct in measuring spectral energy distribution and temperature of faint stars and nebulæ that cannot be determined by other known means.

Last June, Coblentz made some interesting measurements on the heat from planets—a subject that is very obscure. For example, it is thought that Jupiter may be still quite hot, but his measurements with the water cell showed the same transmission for rays coming directly from the Sun, as for rays coming from Jupiter. This means that the atmosphere of Jupiter does not become heated by the Sun's rays and by internal radiation, and that any heat emitted by the planet is trapped by the planet.

Again, the water cell shows that of the total radiation emanating from Mars, 30 per cent is long-wave-length infrared radiation, resulting primarily from warming of the Martian surface by the Sun's rays. In the same manner, it is found that 80 per cent of the radiation from the Moon is to be traced to the heating of the lunar surface by the Sun's rays. The temperature of the lunar surface is probably up to 75°C. to 100°C. when exposed to full sunlight and that of Mars may be 10°C. to 25°C. As for the views held by some of the possibility of vegetation growing on Mars, all depends upon whether we think of palm trees which grow in our tropics or the mosses and lichens which thrive under our arctic snow. So, whether or not we believe that vegetation can exist on Mars, radiometric measurements confirm the conclusions arrived at by astronomers that at Martian moon the snow is melted.

Recently, Abbott and Aldrich using the 100-inch reflector at Mount Wilson and Langley's spectrobolometer, have measured the energy in the spectrum of several bright stars, and estimated stellar temperature up to 10,000°C. This confirms transmission screen measurements of 1921, which simply included wider regions of the spectrum in a single measurement.

As to the usefulness of it all, and the practical applications, —that we cannot foretell. It may give us a clue to attain higher temperatures in our laboratories. The appalling size of a star (300,000,000 miles diameter), the gravitational pressure, the pressure exerted by the light waves, etc., indicate that these high stellar temperatures are owing to dissociation of the stuff of which matter is made. With this as a guide, who will assert that man will never be able to attain higher temperatures than now recorded?

Based upon information from Dr. W. W. Coblentz, Physicist, Bureau of Standards, Washington, D. C.

KINEMATIC MODELS OF ELECTRICAL
MACHINERY

Reducing a Phenomenon to a System of Simultaneous Equations

There are two kinds of problems in physics and engineering, those that can be solved step by step, and those which must be solved by means of simultaneous equations. Problems in arithmetic are mostly of the first kind. In engineering similarly we determine step by step the diameter of a shaft, then the size of a pulley to go on that shaft, then the dimensions of the belt to go over the pulley. In the other class of problems it is necessary to consider simultaneously the relations of two or more variables. For example, the required dimensions of the girder members of a large steel bridge are determined largely by the weight of the bridge. Stresses and weight are two mutually dependent functions, neither of which is known at the start. The usual method of solution is that of successive approximations.

As a boy of eight I insisted to my father that there must be a shorter way of solving arithmetical problems, than by long discussions on the theme of "had the merchant sold five yards less and received 25 cents more." He hesitatingly explained to me how to denote the unknown number of yards by x, and to write and to solve a first-degree algebraic equation. At about the same age I wished to discover short cuts for multiplication of large numbers, so as to have more leisure for multitudinous enterprises in which an active boy engages. I discovered some useful rules; the most helpful of these was how to obtain the square of a number ending in 5.   Thus to find the square of 75, multiply 7 by 7 + 1, and write 25 at the right end.   This gives 5625.

As a Junior in civil engineering in Petrograd I became interested in statically-indeterminate trusses and girders, because it was a problem which could not be solved step by step, either arithmetically or geometrically.   In the Electro-technical Institute in Darmstadt, Germany, in 1899, I became interested in the problem of current and voltage relations in polyphase systems, on unbalanced loads; again because it was a problem that could not be solved step by step, but led to simultaneous vectorial relations.   As a designer of alternating-current machinery and as an investigator of its theory, I have been repeatedly impressed by the similar involved nature of the problems.   All the principal dimensions of a machine and its performance characteristics are so interconnected that one has either to use the method of successive approximations, or to establish and to solve a system of complicated simultaneous equations.

Then the idea of kinematic models for representing the performance of electrical machinery occurred to me.   A number of adjustable kinematic elements, such as rods and disks, may be so connected as to represent a desired equation and to form a system of any number of degrees of freedom.   By interconnecting two or more such systems and by imposing constraints, in the form of guides, the number of degrees of freedom may be limited to two or one, thus giving the characteristics of synchronous and induction machinery respectively.

Then followed several years of efforts to realize these ideas in the form of workable models, first of cardboard, then of wood, and finally of steel bars with brass fittings.   Progress was slow until help came from a special research fund donated to Cornell University by Mr. August Heckscher, of New York. The following kinematic models have been completed:

1. A device for imitating the performance of the electro-magnetic clutch used in Owen magnetic automobiles.

2. The Secomor, which imitates the performance of a polyphase series-connected commutator motor.

3. The Indumor, which imitates the performance of a polyphase induction motor; and its modification, the Shucomor, which represents the performance of a shunt-connected polyphase commutator motor.

4. The Blondelion, which represents the characteristics of a synchronous generator or motor.

5. The Heavisidion, which represents the operating characteristics of a transmission line with distributed capacitance and leakage.

6. The C. P. S.'er (named after Dr. C. P. Steinmetz), for the automatic addition of impedances in series and admittances in parallel.

7. An Integraph based on parallel double-tongs, for mechanical integration or differentiation of a given curve. This device finds its usefulness in problems like "hunting" of machinery, fly-wheel design, ship stability, etc.

An important possibility from use of kinematic models is more rapid improvement of electrical machinery, because the labor of computations for comparative designs is greatly reduced. It is easier to study a range of combinations or to see effects of modifications.

By Vladimir Karapetoff, Professor of Electrical Engineering, Cornell University, Ithaca, N. Y.

MEASURING MOLECULES

A Research in Pure Science Often Has Many and Unexpected Practical Applications

How large are molecules and what are their shapes? The layman frequently expresses incredulity as to practical usefulness of the refined and abstruse work of scientific research. Such incredulity is found even among technical men and other persons whose occupations or fortunes are built upon the sciences. Attempts to solve problems whose industrial importance needs no explanation often are unsuccessful until Science has gone far toward the "root of the matter." Fundamental facts so gained are frequently of wide application.

A modern method for separating copper and certain other metals from some kinds of ores is known as the flotation process. Finely pulverized ore is mixed with water containing a small quantity of oil which forms a persistent froth upon agitation. The solid particles of ore are wet with the oil and these oiled particles adhere to the bubbles of froth. Thus the ore particles float to the top of the tank containing the mixture while the non-metallic particles of the ore, not being wet by the oil, do not adhere to the froth and fall to the bottom of the tank. The remarkable selective action of some oils on certain ores and the effects produced by small quantities of acids and other substances are imperfectly understood.

Some experiments undertaken by Dr. Irving Langmuir in the General Electric Laboratory at Schenectady, have led to the determination of the sizes of molecules of a number of substances and to the proofs of the fact that molecules could not be merely smooth, rigid spheres. It appeared that the dimensions of some molecules differed, the length, for example, in some cases, being several times the square root of the area of the cross-section. It was also evident that the active atoms, or groups of atoms, in certain molecules of a liquid when spread upon the surface of a solid or another liquid, turned in the direction of the surface of contact so as to engage the atoms or molecules in the supporting surface. This knowledge helps to explain why certain liquids will wet each other, and certain solids, but not others—in other words, will spread in a uniform film over the whole surface of contact.

These experiments were undertaken solely because of their scientific interest. Only later was it realized that they had an important bearing on the process of flotation.

These phases of the subject, it will readily be seen, are of importance also in the very practical problem of lubrication, of interest to everybody who runs a machine of any kind. For in order that he may have sold to him the right kind of lubricant, or in order that expensive machinery may not be injured, those who manufacture the lubricants should have the benefit of the chemist's and physicist's knowledge of the fundamental principles developed by such research as that of Dr. Langmuir.

Probably of even wider interest than lubrication, is the subject of painting and varnishing of surfaces of wood, metals and ceramics. Persons who are experimenting upon the nature of paints and other protective coatings for wood, are finding that Dr. Langmuir's studies in connection with the phenomena of flotation are helpful to them also.

But how big is a molecule? To use as an example a commonly known substance, a molecule of castor oil has a cross section in square centimeters expressed by the fraction having 209 for its numerator, and 1 with sixteen ciphers after it for the denominator; its length in centimeters is 5.5 divided by 1 with eight ciphers;—almost too small to be conceived.

Based upon information from Dr. Irving Langmuir, General Electric Company Research Laboratory, Schenectady, New York.

TITANIUM PRODUCTS AND THEIR DEVELOPMENT

AN OLD METALLURGICAL PROJECT REVIVED AND EXTENDED

About 1830, Archibald MacIntyre, David Henderson and associates purchased a large tract of land in Essex County, New York, in the heart of the Adirondack Mountains. This deposit was brought to their attention by Indians, who had visited a small forge in Keene Valley, where iron ore was being smelted. The red men told of a great body of similar material forming a dam near the head waters of the Hudson River. The white men accompanied them to this spot, and having examined the surrounding country carefully, soon arranged for a purchase totalling several square miles.

Despite the extreme ruggedness of the country and the fact that these ore deposits were 40 miles from Lake Champlain, these hardy pioneers in 1840 erected a small charcoal furnace. This furnace was remodelled in 1848, and in 1852 a much larger furnace (11 feet 6 inches × 48 feet) was built and operated successfully, using titaniferous iron ores carrying as high as 18 to 20 per cent titanic oxide. The operation of this furnace was continued until 1856, when, for various reasons, principally lack of transportation, its operation was discontinued.

This old furnace, still standing, in fairly good state of preservation, was recently carefully examined by experts. Their report to the present owners of the property was conclusive that no serious difficulties had been encountered in the smelting of titaniferous ores. The lining shows no sign of scaffolding; the hearth was blown out clear to the bottom, and the slag shows evidence of considerable fluidity.

As years rolled by there grew up a prejudice against the use of titaniferous ores in blast furnace practice, and about 1890 Dr. Auguste J. Rossi, whose name has since become well known because of his work on titanium, was engaged to demonstrate that titaniferous ores could be successfully used in blast furnace practice under more modern conditions. He produced an alloy of iron and titanium, which it was found later was a most efficient deoxidizer and cleanser for the treatment of steel because of the great affinity of titanium for both oxygen and nitrogen, and also because of the property of titanic oxide, formed by the oxidation of titanium, of combining with other slags and oxides and increasing their fusibility, thus effecting their release from the steel by rising to its surface and combining with the slag. The present extensive manufacture and use of ferro-titanium is a result of this pioneer research of Dr. Rossi and indirectly of the early work of MacIntyre, Henderson and their associates.

Some ten or twelve years ago, in the research departments of The Titanium Alloy Manufacturing Company, at Niagara Falls, New York, the extreme opaquing or hiding power of the white pigment, titanic oxide, when mixed with oil was noted. It was found, however, that to manufacture titanic oxide to compete with other opaque white pigments would be practically impossible. Further research demonstrated that a composite pigment consisting of only 25 per cent of titanic oxide thrown down on a base of precipitated barium sulphate, probably because of the wonderful fineness of the particles and maximum distribution of the titanic oxide, actually had approximately 80 per cent of the hiding power of a pigment consisting of 100 per cent titanic oxide.

This research followed by careful tests to demonstrate the availability of this composite titanium pigment brought out the fact that such a pigment had greater hiding power than any white pigment known, was exceedingly inert to various vehicles (oils, etc.) and other pigments, was non-poisonous, and had many properties which made it unique among pigments. After several years of research development, this pigment is now being manufactured in large quantities in this country and Norway.

Already many other uses for the element Titanium have been suggested and no one can safely predict the limit of this development, which originated 75 or 80 years ago, when a few venturesome men attempted the seemingly impossible task of manufacturing iron in the wilderness.

By Andrew Thompson, General Manager, The Titanium Alloy Manufacturing Company, Niagara Falls, New York.

BRIGHTER THAN THE SUN

By aid of the spectroscope astrophysicists are studying the sun and the stars. In order to interpret observations surely, it is necessary to reproduce in the laboratory conditions which give results like those observed through the telescope. In attempts to reproduce high-temperature absorption spectra, such as those of the sun and some stars, J. A. Anderson, of Mt. Wilson Solar Observatory, devised a method for exploding metallic wires by means of electrical discharges. He used fine wires two inches long, of iron, copper, nickel and manganin. Spectra were obtained beyond those previously produced in a laboratory and some striking phenomena were observed in connection with the explosions.

To furnish suitable current, a condenser was built of ninety-eight plates of window glass 16 by 20 inches, having somewhat smaller sheets of tin-foil on each side attached with shellac. This condenser was charged electrically at 26,000 volts. By discharging the condenser through the wire to be exploded, about 30 calories of energy were dissipated in one one-hundred-thousandth of a second. If all this energy had gone into the two milligrams of wire, it would have raised its temperature to approximately 300,000 degrees Centigrade. Actually the flash had an intrinsic intensity of light corresponding to a temperature of about 20,000 degrees, or approximately one hundred times the intrinsic brilliancy of the sun. In spite of this high temperature, the *apparent* absence of heat effects was weird. When copper wires with cotton insulation were exploded, in some cases the insulation was unchanged. Tissue paper wrapped tightly around a wire was torn to bits, but not burned or even charred. The extreme brevity of the existence of the high temperature is the explanation.

If a glass tube with open ends were slipped over the wire, the explosion broke the tube to fragments, which were scattered all over the room. If the ends of the tube were closed with corks and the tube filled with water, the water disappeared completely and the tube was broken into powder so fine as to be unrecognizable as glass. With the wire a few millimeters below the free surface of water in a large glass jar, the sound-wave transmitted through the water by the explosion wrecked the jar. In the circuit with the condenser and the wire to be exploded was a spark gap. The sparks were very noisy. An observer could not go close with impunity unless he protected his ears. This was especially true when a wire was exploded. The sound-wave then sent out could be felt as a distinct sharp blow on the face or hands at a distance of twenty inches or more.

Certain effects accompanying an explosion suggested that the resultant gases when first formed were at high pressures. Efforts were made to measure this pressure by various means. Values of approximately fifty atmospheres (700 pounds per square inch) were determined, when using a nickel wire 0.127 millimeter in diameter. With the smaller iron wires used in many experiments, the pressure was probably of the order of twenty atmospheres.

Consideration of what would happen to a meteoric particle falling into the sun, led to the experiments with the wires. It seemed probable that the path of such a particle within the atmosphere of the sun would not be long, and that the particle would be consumed in a very brief time, probably a fraction of a second. The conditions indicate that a very large quantity of energy is thrown into a small amount of matter in a short time. By electrical means, it seemed possible to throw much energy into a short, fine wire in an extremely brief interval of time. On this basis, the experiments were devised and successfully executed.

Based upon information from Dr. J. A. Anderson, of the Mt. Wilson Observatory, Pasadena, California. For a fuller account of the experiments, see the "Astrophysical Journal," January, 1920.

DECOMPOSING THE ELEMENTS

Some Attempts with the Aid of Electricity

Definitions: *Disintegration*, the spontaneous processes of radio-activity;

Decomposition, the splitting of complex atoms into simpler parts;

Transmutation, some degree of synthesis of atomic nuclei.

Atomic disintegration has been recognized for twenty years. Rutherford established atomic decomposition. To confirm astronomical evidence that heavy atoms are not stable at high temperatures, Wendt and Irion utilized the method of electrically exploding wires, devised by Anderson.* They chose tungsten as the element for experimentation chiefly because its high atomic weight made its decomposition probable on the hypothesis adopted. The wires used were 0.035 millimeter in diameter, about 4 centimeters long and weighed 0.5 to 0.7 milligram.

In these experiments the tungsten wires were exploded within strong glass bulbs so that the products of the explosions could be collected for analysis. The electrical circuit was similar in general to that used by Anderson, but had additional electrical protective devices and a larger condenser. Voltages up to 45,000 were within the possibilities of the equipment, but ordinarily about 30,000 volts were employed. The discharge circuit was so arranged as to allow a rapid non-oscilitating discharge through the tungsten wire to be exploded, in the minimum time, thus concentrating the

* See Research Narrative Number 46.

energy input and giving the maximum temperature in the material of the wire.

The bulbs within which the explosions took place were made of strong Pyrex glass in good spherical form, having a volume of about 300 cubic centimeters. Momentarily, the bulbs had to withstand a tremendous outward pressure. Thick bulbs invariably broke during the explosions because of insufficient elasticity. Thin bulbs immersed in a vessel of water had sufficient support together with elasticity. Three tungsten wire electrodes covered with Pyrex glass were sealed through the wall of the bulb by fusion of the glass. One electrode was used for spectroscopic examination of the gases in the bulb. The two others at opposite ends of a diameter, held the fine wire to be exploded, the ends of the latter being sprung into tiny sockets drilled into the ends of the electrodes.

Then some of the bulbs were exhausted of air until an almost absolute vacuum was obtained, the most efficient devices and methods being used, and the process continued for fifteen hours with each bulb. During this time, the bulb was supported in a furnace and kept at a temperature slightly above 350 degrees Centigrade in order to drive off all gases adsorbed on the interior glass walls. By passage of an electric current during the same period, the wire to be exploded was kept at a temperature above 2,000 degrees. The bulbs so prepared showed no spectrum or fluorescence and no conductance when attached to a 50,000 volt induction coil. Several bulbs when tested were found to have maintained this condition for twelve hours before the explosion.

Other bulbs were prepared by filling with carbon dioxide gas. After the explosion, the gases were passed through a nitrometer for the absorption of the carbon dioxide and the residual gas was analyzed. Although the vacuum method more rigorously excludes contaminations, it does not permit measurement of the volume of gas produced nor the collection of successive samples to form a volume sufficient for chemical analysis.

In a vacuum bulb abundant gas was present after the explosion, but no dust nor smoke nor solid residue was ever found. Visual spectroscopic examination of the contents of the bulb, without opening it, uniformly disclosed faint presence of the strongest green line of mercury, probably from back diffusion from the vacuum pumps. The only other line uniformly present and positively identified, was the strong yellow line of helium. Other, fainter lines, red, blue, violet and yellow were observed, but have not yet been identified. It seems that both hydrogen and neon were absent. (References are to lines of the spectrum.)

In the explosion the fine wire disappeared in a brilliant flash. The gas evolution was very irregular, probably due to irregular conditions of explosion; it is impossible, with the present technique, to produce explosions of uniform brilliancy and temperature. Wendt and Irion, following Anderson's method, went the additional step of so conducting explosions as to collect the products and obtained evidence of the conversion of the metallic tungsten wires into helium to the extent of 50 per cent, or more. The work so far reported is entirely preliminary in nature and is not quantitative. It is, nevertheless, most interesting in its suggestiveness.

Based upon information from Dr. Gerald L. Wendt, Kent Chemical Laboratory, University of Chicago. For a fuller account of the experiments, see Journal of the American Chemical Society, September, 1922.

MALLEABLE IRON

Following a custom that twenty years ago was rapidly gaining ground, a group of founders of malleable iron castings formed the American Malleable Castings Association. Monthly meetings were held; subjects of general interest discussed, and strong bonds of friendship formed. No steps, however, were taken towards improvement of product or study of process, for at that time serious metallurgical research on Iron and steel was confined to institutions of learning and to rich companies or those broadminded enough to anticipate a substantial return from money thus expended.

Development of the bicycle, which had to be light in weight but strong structurally, necessitated alloy steel investigation. The work of Taylor and White on high-speed steels made plain to manufacturer and metallurgist the fact that the threshold of possibilities had hardly been approached by either. The start of the automotive industry carried this message to all that furnished it with material. Inspection that had been desultory became so rigid as to force many manufacturers to improve their product and modernize their plant practice.

There are two principal steps in making malleable-iron castings. First, hard "white" pig iron, mixed with a proportion of steel and cast-iron scrap, is melted in a furnace, and then run into the molds for the castings. Second, these "white" iron castings are cleaned and trimmed and then "heat-treated" by being packed in a mixture of powdered

141

slag and iron oxide in large covered iron boxes, or "pots," placed in an annealing oven, slowly heated to about 1550 degrees Fahrenheit, held at this temperature and slowly cooled, the heat-treatment requiring seven days.

The Association while progressing along certain lines had neglected research, with the result that by degrees the demand for malleable iron had lessened to an extent that became perilous. Eleven years ago, it became apparent to the members that unless scientific principles were substituted for crude practices, within a brief period their tottering industry would crumble. The pretense that they had a secret process was abandoned. It was decided to enter into a thorough research covering the metallurgy of the process, the metallurgical apparatus, and works' practices.

The ultimate tensile strength of the product at that time averaged 39,000 pounds per square inch and the elongation under tensile test 3.5 per cent. As far as could be ascertained there had been no regular mechanical testing. The metallurgy of the process was not well understood. Many founders, indeed, were ignorant of the most vital and elementary details. For the most part the metallurgical apparatus was defective and in many particulars unsuitable. The character of product depended upon hit-or-miss methods. Misconceptions abounded.

A program was laid out. As soon as details could be put into operation, association members were requested to make their "white" iron castings of a composition the elements of which would be restricted to certain limits. These limits were established not only to make sure that the metallurgical change that should take place when the castings were heat-treated unquestionably would be effected, but also to produce a finished product of high ultimate strength accompanied by satisfactory elongation. The members were asked to cast from each "heat" specimens for tensile and impact tests. Through this procedure it was soon possible to ascertain exactly what each member was doing; how he was progressing from month to month, and to compare one member's product with that of the others.

Through painstaking metallurgical research, through design and installation of efficient metallurgical apparatus operated under pyrometric control, through adoption of scientific methods throughout the industry, through introduction of a rational and uniform cost system, and by aid of a competent bureau of Association inspectors, uniform quality can be assured. Although many members can make a product considerably higher in ultimate strength and elongation than the average of the Association, averages only are given here. For the past four years, ultimate strength has been 53,000 pounds per square inch and elongation 15 per cent.

Translated, these figures mean that a declining industry has been restored, has won new fields and has established confidence on scientific fact instead of traditions and secrets which, as so often, were only covers for ignorance. Malleable iron castings are now used for purposes and of sizes and shapes formerly believed impracticable.

Contributed by Enrique Touceda, Consulting Engineer, Albany, New York.

THE UPPER CRITICAL SCORE

First Measurement of the Higher as Well as the Lower Limits of Intelligence, Beyond Which It Is Not Profitable to Employ Applicants for a Particular Type of Job

A rough measure of the brightness, or mental alertness, of an applicant, by means of a standardized mental test, has long been recognized as one of many possible sources of information for use in personnel selection. Early tentative attempts to use this test technique in employment procedure, sometimes met with anomalous results because it was not recognized that, for some types of employment at least, an applicant may be *too intelligent*.

In affiliation with the Carnegie Institute of Technology, Pittsburgh, a group of twenty-seven companies of national scope established, in June, 1916, the Bureau of Salesmanship Research, now the Bureau of Personnel Research. This Bureau was to pool the experience of the coöperators to evaluate their current procedures, and to devise and try out new ways of selecting and developing salesmen. The first year's work, under Walter Dill Scott, issued in a volume of "Aids in Selecting Salesmen," including an improved personal history record, or application form, a model letter of reference to former employers, a guide to interviewing which helped the interviewer to focus his attention on essential traits and to record his judgments quantitatively,* and a set

* This form later became the Scott Rating Scale of the Army.

of five psychological tests with full directions for giving and scoring.

Among these tests was a group intelligence examination, a forerunner of Army Alpha. It was given to various groups of salesmen and sales applicants, and their scores were checked against actual success as measured by amount of sales. Among the men so examined, was a group of 40 salesmen for a food products company. To the dismay of the research workers, when the intelligence test scores were compared with the men's sales-production records, the correlation was almost zero. This appeared to be a severe indictment of the test as a measure of intelligence.

Then came the War, and with it a vast experience in personnel classification and intelligence examining. The psychological tests proved their worth in the Army as indicators of mental alertness. So when C. S. Yoakum, with this background of Army experience, in 1919, assumed direction of the Bureau of Personnel Research, he knew that the intelligence tests methods were valid, and he sought another explanation of the riddle in the findings of 1916. Taking the same data, he computed the correlation between test scores and length of experience with the company. The correlation was not zero. It was negative, −40. The brighter the salesman, the quicker, as a general rule, he left the employ of that concern.

Yoakum repeated the experiment with 76 salesmen of this same company, using the best available adult intelligence examination. The correlation of test scores and length of experience was −46. A job analysis revealed that the work was largely of the routine, order-taking sort. The pay was not large. Chances of promotion were slight. Only the more stolid men were content to remain long enough to get valuable experience and build up a creditable sales record.

Examining the intelligence scores again, it was apparent that there is an upper limit as well as an anticipated lower limit. Within this range, the chances are large that an applicant for a position with this concern will make good. Below this zone he will probably fail for lack of ability. Above it, the probabilities are that he will not remain long enough to learn his work thoroughly and make a good showing. The psychological test had, after all, been a valid measure of mental alertness. The need had been for a determination of its range of utility.

This range varies for different kinds of salesmen, as well as for different occupations. In many jobs it has been shown that there is no upper limit to the optimal intelligence score; but studies of policemen, salesmen, and many types of operatives and clerical workers, where the task is essentially routine, have shown how necessary it is to keep an eye on the upper as well as the lower critical score. Research on the utility of psychological methods in employment and placement is but one of many scientific approaches to problems of industrial personnel. Taken as a whole, the scientific study of the human factor may prove as important to the next era of industrial progress as research in the physical sciences has proven hitherto.

This Narrative was contributed by Dr. W. V. Bingham, Director of Coöperative Research, Carnegie Institute of Technology, and member, Personnel Research Federation.

WOOD AND MOISTURE

CONTROL OF SHRINKING AND SWELLING BY COATING

In many parts of the world, the shrinking, swelling, warping and checking of wood cause much trouble and expense in its many uses, including furniture, vehicles and buildings. As atmospheric or other conditions vary so as to change the moisture in contact with wood, the wood naturally absorbs or gives out moisture, consequently increasing or decreasing its dimensions. To overcome or offset this dimensional change with change of moisture content, men have devised many expedients more or less successful. No generally applicable means have yet been found, however, for completely and permanently preventing changes of moisture content. Furniture and wooden parts of vehicles made for use in New York open their joints, or even come apart, in Arizona. On the other hand, if in course of manufacture the wood were dried to a moisture content suitable for Arizona, not a drawer could be moved in New York.

Wooden blocks are the most suitable mountings for electrotype and other plates from which much printing is done, particularly illustrations. It is highly important that these blocks should not warp or otherwise change dimensions, even minutely. This problem is among those on which the Forest Products Laboratory, of the Department of Agriculture, has been working for years in its endeavors to overcome difficulties encountered in the uses of wood in the arts. One day, one of the laboratory's investigators, as a means of domestic economy, was bronzing the steam-heating radiators in his home. Accidentally he spilled some of the bronze liquid

147

on the "unfinished" top of a kitchen table. Before he could get a cloth to wipe up the spill, the liquid had dried.

This incident soon connected itself in the investigator's mind with his problem at the laboratory. A series of experiments were tried. It was found that a bronze coating, composed of a cheap gloss oil (a bronzing liquid of the gloss oil type) and aluminum powder, was superior to many other moisture-proofing coatings which have been tried. This mixture is very fast drying; three coats can be applied in the course of a half-hour. It is useful, also, for foundry patterns, for backs and unexposed parts of furniture and refrigerators and for similar objects. It is durable only when used indoors; it is not at all resistant to weather. It is cheaper than varnish, enamels or paints. Three coats of aluminum bronze showed an efficiency of 92 per cent in moisture-proofing, no coating being zero.

Some other coatings tested and their efficiencies are of interest: 5 coats of linseed oil, applied hot, followed by 2 coats of wax, 38 per cent; 3 coats of white lead in oil, 54 per cent; 3 coats of spar varnish, 60 per cent; 3 coats of graphite paint, 61 per cent; 3 coats of orange shellac, 87 per cent; a heavy coat of paraffin, 91 per cent; 3 coats of asphalt paint, 96 per cent; 3 coats of spar varnish covered with vaseline, 98 per cent; aluminum leaf with asphalt paint base, also 98 per cent. Of course, the spar-varnish-and-vaseline is suitable only for certain limited temporary purposes. The asphalt paints are inexpensive, but for many uses their blackness is objectionable. Hitherto attempts to find a method for covering asphalt or pitch paints with a coating of more pleasing appearance have failed. In the tests mentioned, coated and uncoated panels of wood were exposed for four-

teen days to an atmosphere having a humidity of 95 to 100
per cent, i.e., extremely damp. The efficiencies are based
on the average quantities of moisture absorbed per unit of
surface area.

Efficient finishing of wood is of great economic importance,
not only for control of dimensions, but also for preservation
from decay and for appearance, as well as for other considera-
tions. After thousands of years of use of wood, so much is
left to be learned that Engineering Foundation, Forest
Products Laboratory, the Bureau of Standards and the industries are initiating a coöperative research of wood-finish-
ing processes. It bears upon the use of wood in buildings,
furniture, farm implements, vehicle wheels and bodies, rail
way cars, and the application of paint, varnish and other
coatings and impregnating materials. It involves knowledge
of the nature of various kinds of wood. More than
$300,000,000 worth of paint and varnish is sold in the United
States every year, a large portion of which is applied to wood.
The value of the wood thus finished and protected, also runs
into hundreds of millions annually. The possibilities of
economy to be realized by scientific study are great. Everybody is concerned.

Based on information supplied by the Forest Products Laboratory,
Madison, Wisconsin, Carlile P. Winslow, Director.

INDEX OF SUBJECTS AND PERSONS